The Kitchen Cupboard Healers

Maxwell Stein

Kitchen Cupboard Healers
Maxwell Stein
Copyright © MMIII de Swartes Ltd, London

Published by The Windsor Group,
The Old School House, 1 St John's Court,
Moulsham Street, Chelmsford,
Essex CM2 0JD

Copyright © MMIII The Windsor Group (This Edition)

Typeset by SJ Design and Publishing, Bromley, Kent

ISBN 1-903904-18-8

Contents

Introduction

MOST PEOPLE probably think of salt, cayenne pepper, vinegar and baking soda simply as condiments found in shakers or bottles in kitchen cupboards across the country. But as well as being seasonings they are far more. They are an essential element in the diet of humans, animals, and even of many plants. They are four of the most effective and most widely used of all food additives, as well as being preservatives and cleansers around the home. Their industrial and other uses are almost without number.

These substances can function individually, or together as a fungicide and insecticide, a fire extinguisher, an animal feed supplement and a water softener. As you'll see in this book, this combination is an extraordinarily versatile substance, and one with a myriad of uses.

Each substance is an invaluable tool for everyday life all around the home. Each has a whole host of handy uses. Once you've started using them, you will wonder how you ever managed without them. The obvious place to make use of them is, of course, in the kitchen. Later in the book, we'll tell you some of our favourite recipes and cooking hints, but in this section, we'll give you some ideas on how to use salt, cayenne pepper, vinegar, and baking soda that really haven't anything to do with cookery, except in the loosest sense. A whistle stop tour of the kitchen reveals any number of handy ways to make use of these most versatile of substances.

SALT

Salt is the common name for sodium chloride, which is manufactured commercially from rock salt, and underground salt beds. As well as being used to flavour and preserve foods, it is used extensively in the commercial world, and in the home as a cleaning agent.

Throughout history, salt has been an important substance in the diet of all living creatures. In fact, researchers consider salt to be so important with regard to our health, that it has been the subject of thousands of medical studies; so much so, the archives in most medical learning establishments are bulging with treatises on the subject.

We have records of the importance of salt in commerce in the Middle Ages and earlier. In some places, like North Africa, trading with salt still continues to this day, thus giving a glimpse of what life may have been like centuries ago.

The earliest human records go back some 4,700 years to when, in China, Peng-Tzao-Kan-Mu published the earliest known treatise on pharmacology. Much of this was dedicated to the method of extracting salt and putting it to general use.

In ancient Greece slaves were sold in the local markets in exchange for salt, hence when slavers asked for too much salt in exchange the expression 'not worth his salt' came about. Other examples include the Arab avowal 'There is salt between us,' the Hebrew expression 'to eat the salt of the palace,' and the modern Persian phrase, namak haram, 'untrue to salt' (i.e., disloyal or ungrateful). In English the term 'salt of the earth' describes a person held in high esteem.

In the past, rulers have recognised the importance of salt in one way or another, and raised vast sums to finance their activities by placing salt taxes on their subjects. It isn't so long ago that salt taxes were imposed by the English monarchs and thousands of subjects were imprisoned for smuggling salt. In France, the French kings developed a salt monopoly by selling exclusive rights to produce it to a favoured few who exploited that right to the point where the scarcity of salt was a major contributing cause of the French

Revolution. In modern times, Mahatma Ghandi defied British salt laws as a means of mobilising popular support for self-rule in India.

In folklore, salt represented life. Hence you never threw salt away, as by doing so, you would be throwing away life itself, which is far too short as it is. Salt was also used in spells to influence the actions of another. For instance, a woman who wished to win back the heart and love of a man who had turned away from her had to throw a pinch of salt into the fire for nine mornings in a row, pronouncing a spell as she did so.

An old gypsy belief was that all children were sick and had no soul until they had been Christened, then the illness would leave the child and his soul would return pure from heaven. Charms such as salt, sand and silver coins were given purposely to prevent the powers of evil from harming the child in any way. Another method of warding off evil was to hang a glass walking stick filled with salt above the entrance to a dwelling.

In religion, salt is the symbol of virtue and purity of the soul. It has played a vital part in religious ritual in many cultures. The Christian Bible has more than thirty references to salt, using expressions like 'let your speech be always with grace, seasoned with salt…' There are many other religious references to salt, including the use of 'holy salt' by the Unification Church.

Salt also had military significance. For instance, it is recorded that thousands of Napoleon's troops died during his retreat from Moscow because their wounds would not heal due to a lack of salt. In 1777, the British Lord Howe was jubilant when he succeeded in capturing General Washington's salt supply.

Today we are very lucky, as the innocuous looking, white granular substance we know as 'salt', is plentiful. It is one of the most easily obtained and least expensive of our necessities.

CAYENNE PEPPER

Cayenne pepper has been produced for thousands of years in the

West Indies and Central and South America. It is made from the dried pods of chilli peppers and other closely related species and varieties of red capsicum in different grades of pungency. In more recent times, the peppers have been grown in all tropical and subtropical countries, and under glass or as an annual in temperate climes.

Cayenne pepper is one of nature's medicaments, and is considered to be one of the most natural, wholesome, ideal stimulants in the medical world.

When taken internally it warms the body, raises metabolism, and increases circulation. The potency of cayenne pepper is considered helpful for various conditions of the gastrointestinal tract, including stomach-aches, cramping pains, and wind. Any known medication cannot equal it when a powerful and prolonged stimulant is needed, as in congestive chills, heart failure, and other conditions calling for quick action. Another benefit that cayenne pepper imparts is its ability to increase the power of all other medicinal and nutritional herbs when taken in combination.

Used in emoluments for rubbing on the skin, cayenne pepper is a traditional, as well as modern, remedy for rheumatic pains and arthritis due to what is termed a counterirritant effect. A counterirritant is something that causes superficial irritation to the skin, thereby relieving deeper inflammation.

As a condiment, cayenne pepper may be called upon for its unique flavour, being much tastier than black pepper. The trick to using this spice is to use it with care and add gradually (a good rule to follow when using any herb or spice). Once you reach the desired taste – stop. The old saying goes you can always add more, but can never take any out. In recipes, whenever a hot stimulant is indicated, cayenne pepper is the favourite ingredient to cook with, especially in Cajun and Creole cookery, both of which originate from South America.

BAKING SODA

Baking soda is frequently confused with baking powder since they both leaven (the process of making bread lighter, thicker and more flavourful).

In fact, baking powder consists of 'baking soda' mixed with 'cream of tarter'. Between them, these acids will react to any cooking situation, and will then work with the sodium bicarbonate within the powder to produce the required leavening effect. Perhaps the best-known use for baking soda is as a leavening agent in baking. When it reacts with an acidic substance, it releases carbon dioxide as a gas; when this occurs during the process of cooking, the food becomes permeated with bubbles. Breads, cakes, biscuits, and other foodstuffs that fix as they cook will all rise, becoming light and airy. The Egyptians, it is believed, were the first to consciously use leavening in their baking and were also the first to use ovens. By the middle of the 3rd Century BC, the Egyptians had developed baking methods that were similar in many ways to those in use today.

Baking soda has several important abilities that make it as useful as it is. Being crystalline, it is abrasive, so it makes an excellent surface cleanser. Its powerful yet gentle action makes it uniquely suited to cleaning a variety of easily scratched surfaces. Because it is alkaline, it is also well suited to breaking down grease and other dirt stains, which are generally acidic in nature. Most nasty smells are also acid-based, and so it functions as an excellent deodorant. This includes organic odours such as sweat, pet waste and rotting food, as well as certain inorganic scents. Combining scouring action, the ability to break down fat and a powerful deodorising function makes baking soda an all-round excellent cleaning agent.

Its anti-acid capabilities also have a wide range of applications. It can be used for purposes as diverse as to relieve the pain of certain insect stings and to prevent corrosion of car battery cables. It also has several medicinal uses, including the relief of acid indigestion, fighting against certain fungal infections and helping to neutralise the pain of sunburn.

VINEGAR

Most people take vinegar for granted, and only a few are interested in the fine taste of best vinegar, and the wide range it can be used to spice dishes, especially salads and fine dressings. From the haute cuisine chefs who prepare food in our top hotels, to those who like to experiment with new recipes, special vinegars or even plain apple cider vinegar, provide new tastes for people to discuss at dinner.

In the past, the use of vinegar has been remarkable and varied. The Babylonians used it as a preservative and as a condiment; they also began flavouring it with herbs to use on their food. Roman legionnaires used it as a beverage as well as for its healing properties. Hypocrites extolled its medicinal qualities and, indeed, it was probably one of our earliest remedies. Biblical references show how it was much used for its soothing and healing properties. In addition, when Hannibal crossed the Alps, vinegar helped pave the way. Obstructive boulders were heated and doused with vinegar, which cracked and crumbled them. As recently as World War I, vinegar was being used to treat wounds. Today it is recommended for treatment of rashes, bites and other minor ailments.

Vinegar is an excellent product for cleaning and disinfecting the skin. It can help fight against persistent skin diseases, and in everyday use, vinegar gives your skin a young and fresh look, by activating the circulation of blood in your skin.

Research chemists value vinegar for its many important properties, and modern industry uses it in many processes, including the manufacture of plastics. It should come as no surprise, then, that it could be used in many everyday chores around the house. Its key constituent, acetic acid, makes it useful in cleaning, deodorising and many other tasks. These are just a few of the ways in which it can help you.

Part One

Around the Home

AS HOUSEHOLD cleansers, salt, vinegar, and baking soda are better than most other expensive products developed over the years. They do not have any harsh abrasive effects, which makes them ideal for cleaning windows, mirrors, glass tops, paint, metal, furniture, and for removing mould and mildew. They are also antiseptic, and are easily and cheaply available.

Air freshener

Place 1 teaspoon of baking soda in a spray bottle and add to it 2 tablespoons of white vinegar and 2 cups of clean water. After the foaming has stopped, replace the spray top and shake well.

Another great air-freshening tip is to stand artificial flowers in a pretty tub ¼ filled with baking soda. The flowers will look great, and you'll be sweetening the air, too. Remember to change the soda once every three months, to keep the action strong and fresh.

When you want to use baking soda as a room freshener, you don't have to use the box it comes in. While it works well to just punch a few holes in the top of the box you don't have to restrict yourself to that. You can make a small packet by placing a quarter of a cup of baking soda in the middle of a 15cm circle of cloth (or inside a coffee filter). Pull the sides up and gather them at the top, before fastening with an elastic band, ribbon or tie, and you've made a pretty deodorant packet.

Alternatively, you can make larger packets by putting a cup of baking soda in the bottom of an old pair of tights. Tie the material just above where the soda fills it, and then tie another knot about an inch above that. Make sure they're secure! You can then put another cup of baking soda in, and tie two more knots in the same way. Once you have enough compartments of soda, just cut the material between each pair of knots, and you'll have made a whole string of handy baking soda sachets that you can keep anywhere to help keep the air fresh.

For larger jobs, you can fill a yoghurt pot, margarine tub or even a shoebox with baking soda, and punch holes in the lid. Remember that you'll need to change it every three months, so write the date of the next change on the top.

Cane furniture

To keep the cane like new, sponge them with a hot liquid of half white distilled vinegar and half water. Place the chairs out in the sun to dry. Salted hot water will have the same effect.

Cupboards

If your cupboards are carpeted, then sprinkle baking soda on the floor there the day before you vacuum them; if they are not, then you can wash the floor down with a mixture of ½ a cup of baking soda and ½ a cup of vinegar in a bucket of warm water to keep them smelling good.

Cut flowers

Cut flowers will keep longer if they are kept in water containing a solution of 1 teaspoon of white distilled vinegar and 1 teaspoon of sugar made up with 570 millilitres of hot water.

Alternatively, add a little salt to the water your cut flowers will stand in for a longer life.

Fireplace

If you have an open fire in the home, it could well be worth keeping an open box of baking soda handy beside it. Not only will it be useful helping to dampen the smell of soot deposits and ashes when you are cleaning out the grate, but it could also prove very useful in case the chimney catches fire, or something small is accidentally set alight. If this happens, throw the soda at the base of the flames; it will help to put them out. Remember never to put yourself in any danger when trying to control fire, and if there is any doubt as to whether the fire is going to spread, always call the fire service immediately.

You can use baking soda made into a paste with water to clean the sooty deposits off the stone or brickwork in and around the fireplace.

Jewellery

For jewellery in general, a thick paste of baking soda and mild shampoo makes a great cleaner. Scrub with an old toothbrush to clean into little nooks and corners. To brighten up gold, sprinkle the piece with baking soda, and then pour vinegar over it and fizz the dirt off before rinsing it clean with water. You shouldn't do this on gemstones or pearls that can't take being soaked. Stones are better brought to a shine by rubbing on a bit of thick baking soda and water paste and polishing up with a dry cloth. This also works well for pearls.

Label gum removal

After removing the label, the residue gum can be easily removed by sponging on white distilled vinegar. Allow the vinegar to soak in for a few minutes and then wash off.

Leather

Polish leather with a spray of undiluted lavender vinegar polished off with a soft duster.

To soften leather combine 150 millilitres of hot lavender vinegar with 150 millilitres of olive oil. Blend well. When cool, wipe the mixture over the leather and rub well into the leather.

Leather articles can be cleaned with a mixture of distilled vinegar and linseed oil. Rub the mixture into the leather and then polish with a soft cloth.

New duster treatment

To enhance the cleaning properties of a new duster, soak it an eggcupful of paraffin and vinegar in equal quantities. Wring the duster out and let it dry. Your duster will absorb dust and give furniture an extra gleam.

Piano keys

Piano keys will come up whiter when wiped with a clean, wet cloth dampened with lemon juice then sprinkled it with a little salt.

Remember that ivory piano keys become more yellow as they age, and so some discolouration is perfectly natural. All that is needed is a gentle cleaning with a paste made from a little baking soda and water. Make sure you don't use too much paste on the cloth at any one time, to avoid dropping any down between the keys.

Plastic covered furniture

If you have plastic-covered chairs, inflatable beds or waterbeds, you'll know that they can start to become discoloured. Baking soda once again comes to the rescue. Dissolve half a cup of baking soda in ¼ litre of water and use this solution to wash the surface. In fact, baking soda is great for cleaning all sorts of plastic surfaces. Simply make a thick paste with water, and use it instead of a commercial cleanser or scourer.

Where you are faced with stubborn stains or deposits, replacing the water with vinegar will give you a stronger-acting, frothy cleanser for getting deep into problem areas.

Rubbish bins

Clean the bin every time it is emptied with a cloth rinsed in a solution of hot water and a tablespoon of baking soda.

Upholstery

The upholstery of your chairs and sofas will also respond wonderfully to a bit of baking soda. Sprinkle the bits of furniture that you want to freshen with baking soda, leave it to work its magic for a minute or three, and then simply vacuum it off. Make sure that the material is dry before you do this, of course.

Venetian blinds

When the time comes to clean Venetian blinds, start by soaking them in a tub of warm water that has had a cup of baking soda added to it. Give them a good scrub on all surfaces with a bath brush, before rinsing them and hanging them to dry. To clean up the cords, rub some baking soda into them by hand while they are still damp.

Walls and woodwork

Baking soda makes a great formulation for cleaning up walls, woodwork and similar painted surfaces. Add ½ a cup to a litre bucket of warm water, along with ½ a cup of white distilled vinegar. If the surfaces are greasy, add a cup of ammonia as well. Wipe this solution on with a sponge or a damp towel, and allow it to permeate for a minute or two before wiping clean. This mixture may not be suitable for all wood finishes; if you have any doubts, try some on an out-of-the-way patch to test for effect. That way, you can be certain of proceeding with confidence.

Window frames, catches, etc

To clean metal frames, catches and other window-related bits and pieces, scrub them with a wet brush that has been dipped into baking soda. Rinse them off with a wet sponge before drying.

The Kitchen Environment

No matter how neat and tidy you are, the kitchen is one place that takes up much of your time. Washing up is a daily chore, and it seems so never-ending. You've hardly had time to turn around from washing one lot of pots and pans when the sink or dishwasher is full again. Sometimes it seems like a constant running battle between the forces of cleanliness and some malicious gremlin of dirty plates. Fear not, however; the famous quartet is at hand to add power to your arm.

Fire prevention

Baking soda makes a great extinguisher for smaller fires. Keep a large, open box handy near the cooker. Water is dangerous to use in cooking fires, because it won't stop electrical fires, and it will worsen oil fires. Baking soda can be used in both cases. Throw handfuls of it at the base of a fire to smother it quickly, or dump in onto a burning pan, but always make sure that you keep your distance. You should also make sure that you don't use it for a fire in a deep-fat fryer, for while it is good for small grease fires, a deep fire could splatter and spread the flames. If in doubt, always call the fire service.

Ovenproof glass or porcelain casserole dishes

To loosen hard-to-clean baked on food on heatproof glass or porcelain casserole dishes, boil ¼ cup of white distilled vinegar with 2 cups of water in the dish and leave overnight. Wash afterwards in hot, soapy water.

Pots and pans

- ❏ Soak normal food-stained pots and pans in full strength white distilled vinegar for 30 minutes. Afterwards, rinse in hot, soapy water. For pots and pans that have burnt-on food, cover the bottom with equal quantities of water and vinegar. Bring the liquid to the boil; remove from the heat and leave to soak overnight. The next day, wash in hot soapy water.

- ❏ Alternatively, to remove burned on food from a pan, let the pan soak in baking soda and water for 10 minutes before washing. On the other hand, scrub the pot with dry soda and a moist scouring pad.

- ❏ For a badly-burned pan with a thick layer of burned on food; sprinkle a thick layer of baking soda directly onto the bottom of the pan, then sprinkle on just enough water so as to moisten the soda. Leave the pot overnight, and then scrub it clean next day.

- ❏ Polish up your stainless steel pots and pans by cleaning them with a cloth that has been rinsed in a solution of 1 part water and 2 parts white distilled vinegar.

- ❏ To clean up non-stick pans, make a paste of baking soda and water, transfer the paste to a cloth, and scrub the pan gently. It will lift off the grease, but won't harm the coating. This will also get rid of persistent flavours that have worked their way into the non-stick lining. Where you have stubborn stains to contend with, mix up 2 cups of water with 3 tablespoons of baking soda and boil this in the pan for 10 minutes. If the stain proves to be stubborn, add a ½ cup of bleach. Make sure that you don't let the pan boil dry when you do this, though.

- ❏ For white enamel cookware, you'll need to use 2 cups of white distilled vinegar and 2 tablespoons of baking soda, and you'll need to boil it for up to 10 minutes if there are persistent stains.

❑ To restore the sheen of copperware, sprinkle the pots with baking soda, and then pour some white distilled vinegar over it. Leave this to stand for 10 or 15 minutes, and then scrub the mixture off (and over the sides) using ½ a lemon as your brush. Alternatively, you can always just sprinkle the soda straight onto the lemon to make a great cleaning pad for any bits of copper or brass that you want to clean up.

Roasting trays

To clean up a dirty roasting tray with almost no effort, first sprinkle baking soda generously over the tray. Leave it for a moment, and then mix a cup of water with ¼ cup of white distilled vinegar, and pour it into the tray. It'll fizz up, and lift the grease straight off.

Rubbish bins

One of the most malodorous parts of any kitchen is the rubbish bin. One great way of helping to keep it smelling fresh is to sprinkle the bottom of the bin with baking soda whenever you change the dustbin liner. Similarly, if you have a rubbish compactor, add a tablespoon of baking soda each time you crush a load down to help keep it smelling pleasant. You can even add a second tablespoon between crushes if the rubbish is particularly smelly.

Rust marks

Rust can be removed from appliances or from patches on the floor by scrubbing with a thick paste of baking soda and water.

When it comes to declogging the bases of taps, window catches, or other small, fiddly bits of metalwork that may have rusted, cover the object with baking soda, and then gently pour white distilled vinegar over it. Leave it alone until it stops fizzing, then scrub at it with a small brush or an old toothbrush, and just lift the rust off.

For the metal legs of chairs or tables, make a thick paste of baking soda and white distilled vinegar, and wipe it onto the affected area. Scrub at it with a little wad of aluminium foil, before wiping it clean with a piece of kitchen towelling.

Silver tableware

Baking soda is also great for bringing the shine back to silver cutlery. Place the pieces on a sheet of aluminium foil in your sink, then sprinkle them with baking soda and add some hot water to cover. Leave them to sit for ten minutes, and they will regain their shine. If it seems stubborn, a light sprinkling of salt will help. Try not to use an aluminium pan, because whilst baking soda will clean some aluminium, it will darken other bits.

You can treat individual pieces of silver cutlery by cutting a raw potato in half, dipping the cut end in baking soda, and using this as a rubbing pad. If you don't have potato handy, then you can make do with a thick paste of baking soda and a damp sponge. Either way, you then rinse the piece and dry it up to a lovely polish.

Sinks

- An open box of baking soda tucked under the sink and changed every 3 months or so can prove a great way of fighting the stale, mouldy smells that can come from that area of the kitchen.
- Once you've finished with the dishes, baking soda can still lighten your workload by helping to keep the sink itself clean and fresh. Fill the bottom of the sink with water, and add a couple of tablespoons of baking soda. Use this solution to wipe down the sink, and rinse your sponges and dishcloths in it too.
- If the sink needs a proper clean, baking soda paste makes a great replacement for a cream cleanser. Unlike many scouring solutions, it will not scratch stainless steel. If your sink is porcelain, then you can use baking soda to help

remove stains and whiten it up. Cover the sink surface with paper towels and pour a small amount of bleach onto them, so that they become dampened through. Allow these to stand for 10 minutes, then remove and discard them, rinse the sink with water, and then sprinkle on baking soda. Wipe this off with a damp sponge to remove the last remnants of the bleach.

❑ If your sink becomes clogged, or you have a problem with trapped particles of food leaving an unpleasant smell, then there are ways to help. One swift way to improve the situation is to heat a cup of white distilled vinegar in a microwave, then pour a cup of baking soda down the plughole, following it up with the hot vinegar. Wait for 5 minutes, and then pour ½ litre of boiling water down after them.

❑ If your problems require a slightly stronger answer, then mix baking soda and salt together in equal amounts. Pour a cup of this mixture down the plughole, and leave it alone overnight. In the morning, wash it through with a litre of boiling water. If you are going away for a while, pouring a bit of baking soda down the sink as you leave will make sure that the drain stays fresh for when you return.

Teapots and teacups

To clean the tannin stains or rust build-ups out of a teapot, fill it with 2 tablespoons of baking soda and a quarter of a cup of white distilled vinegar, then top this up with water. Boil gently for about 15 minutes, or longer if the stains are stubborn. Rinse afterwards for a shiningly clean effect.

Baking soda also works very well for teacups. Rub a thick paste onto the deposits, leave it for a minute or so, and then simply wipe the soda – and the stain – away.

Walls and ceiling

When it comes to cleaning the walls and ceiling of your kitchen, caked-on grease and water stains can provide a real challenge to the ingenuity. One traditional recipe for a cleaning solution that still beats most of the commercial cleaners you can buy in the shops today is to make a mix of equal measures of baking soda, powdered chalk, wood ash and pumice stone. This powder is then pasted onto the surface you want to clean using a piece of raw potato. When you wipe it off, you'll wipe off all the dirt and stains with it.

Glass and Crystal

Bottle cleaning

- Clean away the stains in small-necked bottles by pouring white distilled vinegar into the bottle and shaking. For tougher stains, add a teaspoon of baking soda and shake vigorously. Rinse thoroughly and repeat until clean.
- Clean stained glass vases by soaking them in vinegar, a squeeze of washing-up liquid, and very hot water. Dry with a cloth as soon as you can touch the hot glass and they will be clear again.
- Give baby bottles a good cleaning with 1 teaspoon of baking soda and hot water. Rinse well before using again.

Carpets

- To make a homemade shampoo, add 1 cup of vinegar to 5 litres of water. Clean the carpet with a soft brush dipped in the solution. In case the carpet colours are not fast, always test on an inconspicuous area of the carpet before using.
- When cleaning a carpet with any commercial shampoo add 2 tablespoons of white distilled vinegar to the rinse. The carpet

will stay fresh longer, because it removes any detergent residue.

- Baking soda makes a wonderfully versatile carpet cleaner. For a general-purpose carpet shampoo, add ½ a cup of baking soda to 1 litre of water. Where the carpet is extra grimy, sprinkle it with a small amount of the mixture after you have dampened the carpet, and allow it to soak for a minute or two before scrubbing away the grime. Make sure that the material can cope with this by first testing a small patch somewhere where it will not be noticed. Dampen the carpet, sprinkle some baking soda on the test patch, and leave it for five minutes. Scrub it out after the time has passed, and check that the colour in the carpet hasn't been distorted or bleached.

- Bring up the pile and make your carpets look like new by brushing them with a mixture of 1 cup of white distilled vinegar in a litre of water.

- Dissolve chewing gum on carpets, by applying hot vinegar to the gum and then scraping it off with a scraper.

- If you are unfortunate enough to have to deal with vomit, making sure that there is no lasting stain or smell is an important priority. Remove as much debris as you can, and then sprinkle plenty of baking soda over what remains. Working from the edges inwards, scrub in with a stiff brush, rinsing what you have brushed with a clean sponge. You will need to rinse the sponge several times. Soak up the moisture with kitchen roll or other absorbent paper towelling. Once you have finished this, sprinkle a light layer of baking soda over the patch, and leave it; once it is dry, vacuum it up.

- If pet fleas are an issue, then try adding oil of rosemary to the baking soda to drive them away. The best way to distribute the soda evenly is to use a sieve or a flour shaker. There's no need to worry about colourfastness; so long as the carpet remains dry, the baking soda will stay inert, and will just absorb smells.

❏ Baking soda is also a wonderful tool for keeping your welcome mats clean and fresh. For ones indoors, spread baking soda on them, let it stand for a while, and then simply vacuum it up. For ones outside, it's even simpler, rub the soda in with a stiff broom, and then you can either hose it out of the mat, or leave the mat to wait for some rain!

China and glassware rinse

Keep your china and fine glassware sparkling clean by adding a cupful of white distilled vinegar to a bowl of warm water. Gently rinse the china or glassware in the solution and let dry.

Crystal

Wash in a solution of 1 part white distilled vinegar to 3 parts water. After washing, add a tablespoon of white distilled vinegar to the water when rinsing. It will give it that extra sparkle.

Cutting boards

Cutting boards can be kept clean and safe with baking soda. Sprinkle a generous amount over the board, then pour vinegar over it. Allow it to fizz itself clean for a few minutes, and then rinse it off with hot water.

Decanters

To clean out decanters, fill with a solution of warm water and white distilled vinegar in equal parts mixed with half a cupful of baking soda. Shake hard and leave to stand for half an hour. Wash and rinse when the decanter is considered to be clean.

❏ Bring up the pile and make your carpets look like new by brushing them with a mixture of 1 cup of white distilled vinegar in a litre of water.

- ❑ Dissolve chewing gum on carpets, by applying hot vinegar to the gum and then scraping it off with a scraper.
- ❑ If you are unfortunate enough to have to deal with vomit, making sure that there is no lasting stain or smell is an important priority. Remove as much debris as you can, and then sprinkle plenty of baking soda over what remains. Working from the edges inwards, scrub in with a stiff brush, rinsing what you have brushed with a clean sponge. You will need to rinse the sponge several times. Soak up the moisture with kitchen roll or other absorbent paper towelling. Once you have finished this, sprinkle a light layer of baking soda over the patch, and leave it; once it is dry, vacuum it up.
- ❑ If pet fleas are an issue, then try adding oil of rosemary to the baking soda to drive them away. The best way to distribute the soda evenly is to use a sieve or a flour shaker. There's no need to worry about colourfastness; so long as the carpet remains dry, the baking soda will stay inert, and will just absorb smells.
- ❑ Baking soda is also a wonderful tool for keeping your welcome mats clean and fresh. For ones indoors, spread baking soda on them, let it stand for a while, and then simply vacuum it up. For ones outside, it's even simpler, rub the soda in with a stiff broom, and then you can either hose it out of the mat, or leave the mat to wait for some rain!

Insect deterrent

Deter garden ants from the kitchen by washing work surfaces, cabinets and floors with white distilled vinegar.

Linoleum – unwaxed

Wipe the surface over with a cloth that has been rinsed in a solution of 2 tablespoons of white distilled vinegar and 2 litres of clean hot water. The black scuffmarks that the soles of some shoes leave behind on lino floors can also be easily removed using a baking soda and water paste. For tougher stains, such as ink spills, the best procedure is to apply a nearly dry paste to the mark and let it sit for a while before scouring the mark with a cloth dipped in baking soda.

Painted surfaces

Painted cabinets come sparkling clean if wiped down with a soft cloth rinsed in a solution of 1 litre of hot soapy water, 1 tablespoon of baking soda, and 3 tablespoons of white distilled vinegar.

Regular rubbing with baking soda made into a paste can keep scratches in almost any surface clean – and so less noticeable.

Plastic surfaces

- ❏ Wipe everyday grime from plastic surfaces with a cleaning duster dampened with a solution of half white distilled vinegar and half soapy water.
- ❏ Plastic can also be cleaned with dry baking soda on a damp cloth. Rinse and dry after cleaning.
- ❏ Plastic can be cleaned and made anti-static by wiping down with a solution of 1 tablespoon of white distilled vinegar to 1 litre of water. This will cut down on the plastics' tendency to attract dust.
- ❏ Laminated surfaces and other plastics can also be cleaned with the aid of a lemon; get a fresh one, cut it in half, and squeeze the juice onto the surface. Spread it evenly, and then leave it for half an hour. When the time is up, sprinkle it with baking soda, and scrub the surface with the mixture. Rinse the surface and dry it to finish.

Quarry tiles

For a cheap to produce floor tile cleaner take 1 part white distilled vinegar, 1 part rubbing alcohol, 1 part water, and a squeeze of dishwashing liquid. Mix this into a spray bottle and just spray and clean.

To remove the white patches that form on quarry tiles, mix 1 tablespoon of vinegar with 570 millilitres of water. Dampen a cloth with the solution and give the tiles a good hard rub. Leave to dry. If necessary, repeat the treatment one more time.

Surface cleaners

Keeping surfaces looking clean and smelling fresh can be quite a chore. They can even become a bit of a health hazard. Baking soda and vinegar can help.

Thermos bottle cleaner

Wash out thermos bottles and cooling containers with a solution of 1 tablespoon of baking soda and hot water to get rid of stale smells.

Water marks inside fragile vases

Stains inside fragile vases and glasses that need special care can be removed by placing a tea towel soaked in white distilled vinegar inside the vase or glass so it has contact with the sides. Let it remain for an hour or two and the stains should wipe away with ease.

Windows, mirrors, and glass-tops

To clean up windows and bits of glassware, one wonderful tactic is to wash them down with a wet cloth sprinkled with baking soda. Rinse the window afterwards and then rub it down to dry it off. A nice sparkle is guaranteed. Remember, when you are dealing with glass, that if you don't dry it properly, the water will evaporate and leave small stains, so your good work will be undone.

Alternatively, you can clean glass mirrors, glass tops and windows by adding 2 tablespoons of vinegar to a small bucket of warm water. To finish off, buff the surface with a clean, dry cloth.

Wooden surfaces

To keep wooden surfaces clean, pour some baking soda onto a damp sponge and use it to rub away dirt, stains and nasty smells. Rinse afterwards with plain water.

Household appliances

Appliance cleaners

No matter what you are up against, you can rely on salt, vinegar and baking soda for a helping hand. For a powerful appliance cleaner, make a mixture of ¼ cup of baking soda, ½ cup of white distilled vinegar, 1 cup of ammonia, and 1 litre of water. Make this up in a bucket, and use it as a general wash. The results will be astonishing.

All white appliances have a tendency to yellow with age. Make a mixture of four cups warm water and half a cup of baking soda and sponge it onto the appliance that you want to clean. Let it stand for ten minutes or so, and then rinse it off. All the yellowing will come off with the soda, and you'll be left with a nice, clean appliance.

Barbecue grill cleaner

Wipe the grill over with a wet cloth, then sprinkle baking soda over the surface, leave for ten minutes, then rinse off. The burnt-on grease should just wipe away.

Blenders

Automatic blenders are often very hard to properly clean, particularly if you've been chopping something pungent, such as fish or onions. One handy way to give it a good clean-out is to fill it up to the half-way mark with water, then add one teaspoonful of baking soda and a small drop of some detergent. Fix the lid down, and turn the blender on for a minute or two. Pour out the solution, give it a quick rinse around, and the blades will be clean and fresh.

Coffee maker cleaner (automatic)

When hard water mineral deposits start affecting the automatic drip in your coffee maker, fill the reservoir with white distilled vinegar and run it through a brewing cycle. Rinse thoroughly with clean water when the cycle is finished. (Check the manufacturer's manual for specific instructions before cleaning)

Coffee maker cleaner (percolator)

When the taste of percolated coffee becomes stale and bitter, it is due to residue and oils that collect inside the percolator. Cleaning can be done by filling with white distilled vinegar and leaving overnight. In the morning, rinse thoroughly and wipe with a damp cloth.

Coffee pot cleaner – general

- Wash glass or stainless steel coffee pots (but not aluminium) in a soda solution comprising 3 tablespoons of baking soda to 1 litre of water.
- Run your coffee maker through its cycle with a solution of 1 tablespoon of hot water. Then rinse. If there are stains you want to get rid of, follow this up by boiling ½ litre of water with a cup of lemon juice added to it. Between the two treatments, the machine will be sparkling.
- For coffee filter baskets, a more direct approach is advised. Rinse the basket out, and then instead of drying it, sprinkle it with baking soda. Leave it for 15 minutes to set, and then brush the soda out with an old toothbrush, so that you really get all the nooks and crannies clean. Rinse it off once you've finished.

Cookers

- ❏ One of the most stubborn surfaces to clean is the top of your cooker. Glass-topped cookers can be kept shop-clean with the use of baking soda and water paste. An old toothbrush used as a scrubbing brush makes it really simple to get into all the corners. Caked-on oil comes off quickly with baking soda, particularly if you add some white distilled vinegar to the paste to give it some zing. If the deposits are baked on, then wet them first with water before sprinkling on the baking soda. Leave it for 10 or 15 minutes, and they'll be as easy to wipe away as if they were just a fresh splash. Remember to make sure that there's enough water to soak into the encrustation, of course! Anywhere there's a splatter, there's a handy use for baking soda.

- ❏ If you have trouble with clogged gas nozzles on a gas cooker, they can be quickly unblocked by boiling them in a pan that contains a strong solution of baking soda – say ¼ of a box in ½ litre of water. You can also add a little baking soda to the drip catchers under the nozzles of a gas stove. Not only will it get rid of any rancid smells and make them easier to clean up, but it will also help to prevent fire. Similarly, sprinkling the bottom of your oven with a small amount of baking soda will help to fight off smells and make drips of fat easier to clean up.

- ❏ Major oven spills can be easily dealt with by covering them with baking soda while they remain fresh and damp. Let them stand for a while, and then simply sponge them off.

- ❏ When the time comes to give your oven a deep clean, one excellent tactic is to leave a cup of ammonia overnight in a cold oven. In the morning, remove it and sprinkle the shelves and surfaces with baking soda. Let it stand for a moment, and then wipe down the surfaces with a damp cloth or paper towel, and watch the caked grease just come off.

- If you want a slightly faster tactic, then you can soak a scouring pad with vinegar, and sprinkle salt onto the top. Then all you have to do is to wipe the oven clean!
- Glass oven doors can be degreased nice and easily by covering with baking soda and then wiping down with a wet cloth. If the grease is stubborn, leave the wet cloth on the surface, over the baking soda, for a minute or two to give it a good chance to soak into the muck and do its work.
- Oven drip-trays and grill racks require stern treatment. Don't fight with them in the sink; instead, tie them in a plastic rubbish bag and take them outside. Add a mixture made from 1 cup of baking soda and ½ cup of ammonia, and leave them overnight. All the grime will wipe straight off the next morning.
- For everyday cleaning, dampen your cleaning cloth in equal amounts of white distilled vinegar and water and use it to wipe out your oven.

Deep-fat fryer

Dispose of as much oil from the fryer as possible (remember to always make sure it is cold first), and then sprinkle it with baking soda and salt. Use a cloth to wipe it up. Once you've done that, a quick slosh around with hot soapy water and a rinse should restore the fryer to a pristine condition – and the surfaces won't be scratched, either.

Dishwashers

If you have a dishwasher, you can still put baking soda to excellent use. If you mix it in equal parts with borax, it makes an excellent – and thrifty – dishwashing powder. To give extra oomph to your normal washing cycle, you can also sprinkle some baking soda over the dishes before you wash them, and also a little into the bottom of the machine. This will help to boost the action of the first cycle, and will keep the machine fresh. If you specifically want to give the dishwasher itself a clean, then simply pour half a box of baking soda into the bottom, and then set the machine, empty, on a normal washing cycle. That will neutralise any nasty smells that may be lingering.

Similarly, baking soda can keep the machine fresh if you are going to be away for a while. Sprinkle a little around the machine, and leave the door open a chink. That will make sure that it doesn't get musty in there for when you return.

Electric iron cleaner

Heat a mixture of 1 part salt with 1 part white distilled vinegar in a small aluminium pan. Use on a clean cloth for cleaning the base of electric irons, flat irons, etc.

Extractors

Clean away grease and dirt from exhaust fan grills, air-conditioner blades and grills with a cloth rinsed in ½ litre of hot water and 3 tablespoons of baking soda. Add some neat white distilled vinegar to the cloth when in use. This also works for the meshing over smoke extractors, and other bits and pieces which are coated on with hardened grease and dirt.

Kettle furring

Kettles always fur-up with lime deposits in hard water areas. Pouring half a cupful of white distilled vinegar into the kettle, and topping it up with water can easily remove this deposit. Allow the water and vinegar to boil then leave for an hour or so. Rinse the inside of the kettle thoroughly before using.

If you have a kettle with an automatic switch, then wait thirty seconds and boil it again, and do this four or five times. Once you've finished, pour the mixture out, and rinse it well.

Microwave ovens

Baking soda is great at keeping your microwave clean. A solution of four tablespoons of baking soda in two pints of warm water makes a great wash for wiping the inside of your microwave. In fact, you can keep an open container of baking soda in your microwave when it isn't being used, to help absorb all those smells. Don't leave it while you're cooking, of course; you should always take it out, but put it right back in afterwards. If you don't like the ugly box on your surface while you are using your microwave, then pour the baking soda into an attractive container. That way it'll look good on your worktop while you are cooking. If you put the baking soda right in the middle of the oven, you won't be able to forget it's there when you are preparing to use the machine.

To give the microwave a really thorough cleansing, put a tablespoon of baking soda in a mug full of water (make sure the mug is microwave safe), and then boil the contents in the microwave for 4 or 5 minutes. When you've finished, all the insides of the microwave will be damp with soda-laden steam, and just right for wiping down with a cloth to clean the machine thoroughly.

If a spill becomes baked onto the microwave, splash it with water, and then sprinkle some baking soda on top of it. Leave it for a few minutes, and then come back to it; you'll find that it is easy to lift off.

Refrigerator cleaner

❑ In the fridge, baking soda has a multitude of uses. Open a box and prop it in a handy corner. The soda will absorb all the smells, keeping your fridge – and your food – fresh and healthy. You can do the same in the freezer, too. When you use baking soda like this, it is best to change it every three months. To help yourself remember when it is time to say out with the old and in with the new, write the date that it's due for change on the side.

❑ If the worst comes to the worst and something really goes off in your fridge – some spilt milk goes sour, for example – then to clean the smell off the walls, wash the shelves and the inside of the fridge with a solution of ½ cup of baking soda in 250ml of warm water. The drip-tray under your icebox compartment can also get pretty unpleasant. Sprinkle it liberally with baking soda to make sure it stays fresh.

❑ You can also make the most of baking soda to help with your vegetable box. Sprinkle a layer of soda at the bottom of your vegetable compartment (the plastic bin) of your fridge. Cover this with a double layer of kitchen towel. You'll need to change this every quarter too, so write the change date on the towelling in felt-tip pen when you put it down.

❑ When you have an odour lingering in one of the compartments in your fridge, you can sanitise it by filling it with very hot water, and adding 1 tablespoon of baking soda, 1 tablespoon of vinegar, and a few drops of detergent. Leave it for half an hour before rinsing it clean.

❑ When you defrost your fridge or freezer for its regular cleaning, be sure to wash all around all the sides and shelves with a solution of 5 tablespoons of baking soda in ½ litre of water. It'll help to maintain a fresh and pleasant atmosphere for your food.

❑ Where spills leave stains, or perhaps rust sets in inside your fridge, a thick paste of baking soda and white distilled vinegar can be used as a wonderful stain remover and gentle scouring powder.

Septic tanks

If you have a septic tank, use vinegar instead of harsh chemicals to clean the toilet bowl. Let it set overnight if you can; it will help keep germs down.

Steam irons

To keep the steam jets in a steam iron free of water sediments, pour equal amounts of white distilled vinegar and water into the iron's water chamber. Turn to steam and leave the iron on for 5 minutes in an upright position. Then unplug and allow to cool. Any loose particles should come out when you empty the water.

Sink disposal unit cleaner

Sink disposal units can be kept clean and odour free with vinegar ice cubes. Make the cubes by filling an ice tray with a mixture of 1 cup of vinegar and enough water to fill the ice tray. When frozen, put a few vinegar ice cubes down the disposal at the end of the day, then flush it with cold water for a minute or so.

Waffle and toasted sandwich makers

When it comes to cleaning iron plates, such as waffle grills or toasted sandwich makers, sprinkle baking soda on directly and then scrub it with an old toothbrush. This will make sure that you get to all the various corners and crannies, and will remove any bits of stuck-on bread, waffle or whatever, so as to leave you with a clean and stick-free plate.

Washing machine cleaner

Once a month, add 1 litre of vinegar and ½ a cupful of washing soda to the washing machine and run for a full cycle at 60°C to clean soap film from the heating element and hoses. It's a good idea to place a large white towel, or something similar in the machine for the drum to maintain a proper balance.

Metal polishes

Brass

Brass will shine like new if polished with the following paste. Dissolve 1 teaspoon of salt in 1 cup of white distilled vinegar and stir in enough flour until it becomes a paste. Apply the paste to the metal and let it stand for about 15 minutes. Then rinse with clean warm water and polish until dry.

To clean brass lamps, unscrew sections, and soak in bucket of 1 part white distilled vinegar to 10 parts water. All green and black tarnish comes off in no time.

Chromium

Chromium-plated articles will clean and polish up if cleaned with a cloth soaked in white distilled vinegar.

In the days when cars had lots of chromium plated parts this was the favourite cleaner to keep the chrome looking spanking new. Prepare a paste using white distilled vinegar mixed with one tablespoon of flour and two teaspoons of salt. Add enough vinegar to make a thick paste. Apply to the metal with a clean cloth.

Copper polisher

Mix together equal quantities of lemon juice and white distilled vinegar. Clean the copper with a paper towel dampened with the solution. Polish with a soft, dry duster.

Cutlery polisher

Make up a solution of 2 tablespoons of white distilled vinegar with 1 teaspoon of baking powder and 2 cups of hot water. Immerse the cutlery in the solution and then rinse in hot, soapy water.

Pewter

Prepare a paste using white distilled vinegar mixed with 1 tablespoon of flour and 2 teaspoons of salt. Add enough vinegar to make a thick paste. Apply to the metal with a clean cloth, allow to dry and then buff.

Silverware

Polish silverware with dry baking soda on a damp cloth. Rub, then rinse and dry. For silver pieces without raised patterns or cemented on handles: place the silver on aluminium foil in an enamel pot. Add boiling water and 4 tablespoons baking soda. Let stand, rinse and dry.

This method is in fact unpopular with some people because it is too good; it cleans all the tarnish off, making detailed etched edges slightly trickier to see. You may want to bear this in mind.

Stains

Basic stain removers

Don't give non-oily stains a chance to dry into the fabric. Apply a mixture of one teaspoon of liquid detergent and 1 teaspoon of white distilled vinegar in a pint of lukewarm water to remove the stain. Apply with a soft cloth and rub gently. Rinse with a towel moistened with clean water and blot dry. Repeat this procedure until the stain is gone. Then dry quickly, using a fan or hair dryer.

For oily stains, make up a solution of 150 millilitres white distilled vinegar with 1 teaspoon of baking soda and 1 teaspoon of salt. Lightly rub the stain with a clean cloth soaked in this solution. Soak the stain with clean water after the stain is removed and allow to dry.

Blood stains on clothing

Blood stains can be persistent. Wet them with a little cold water, and rub dry baking soda into them once they are dampened. Providing the fabric can cope with it, follow this up by rubbing in a little hydrogen peroxide, too.

Carpet stains

- ❑ Tree sap from Christmas trees can easily be cleaned from carpets, once you have checked that they won't be discoloured. Make a paste of baking soda and water, and spread it on the sap. Leave it until the sap has been absorbed; then vacuum the remnants of the paste from the carpet.
- ❑ Wine spills and grease stains also respond well to baking soda. Soak up as much of the spill as you can as quickly as possible, and then sprinkle the patch with baking soda immediately afterwards. Lay enough down to absorb any moisture with a little to spare. Leave it on for a while, and then vacuum up the remnants.
- ❑ For more proactively acidic spills, such as battery acids, toilet cleaners, drain cleaners and so on, the most important thing is to stop your carpet being eaten away, so soak the area with cold water. Don't use warm water, because that will speed up the acid's reaction. Once you've watered the area, cover it generously with baking soda, and leave it to neutralise the now-diluted acid. Once everything is dry, the baking soda should vacuum up from the carpet.

Coca cola stains

When cotton, cotton polyester and permanent press fabrics become stained with spilt coca cola drinks, sponge the stain with white distilled vinegar until it disappears. Then clean according to the directions on the manufacturer's label.

Crayon marks on fabrics

Crayon can be removed from most fabrics by rubbing very gently with a damp cloth sprinkled with baking soda.

Deodorant stains

Deodorant and anti-perspirants stains may be removed from clothing by lightly dabbing with white distilled vinegar before washing.

Footwear

To tackle grass, it is better to use a paste of baking soda and water and to scrub at the stains with an old toothbrush. Boots are particularly prone to this problem, for obvious reasons. You can get rid of scuff marks in general from your shoes in the same way, by scrubbing with a paste.

Suede can also benefit from the use of baking soda; rub it in with a gentle brush, let it sit for a while, and brush it out again.

Glassware

Soak discoloured glass in a salt and vinegar solution to remove stains.

Grease stains on polyester fabrics

To remove grease stains from polyester fabrics, simply rub baking soda into the spot and then brush the soda, and the grease, straight off.

Ink stains on leather

To get rid of unwanted ink stains, lie the item out flat and sprinkle baking soda over the patch. Leave it to absorb the ink for a while, then brush it off, and repeat if necessary.

Ink stains on fabrics

- Stained cotton, cotton polyester and permanent press fabrics can be saved if they are sponged with white distilled vinegar within 24 hours and washed immediately.
- Dried on stains need to be soaked in milk for 1 hour. Make up a paste with white distilled vinegar and cornflour. Cover the stain with the paste and, when it has dried, wash the fabric in the normal way.
- Pour a mound of salt on an ink spot on your carpet; let the salt soak up the stain.

Marble surfaces

- To remove light stains, rub with undiluted white wine vinegar. Leave the vinegar on the surface for a few minutes then rinse thoroughly with clean water.
- To remove stubborn stains from marble, scour with a paste of soda and water.
- Or, wash marble-topped furniture with a solution of 3 tablespoons of baking soda in 1 litre of warm water. Let stand awhile, then rinse.

Oil and grease stains

Oil and grease washes out better with baking soda added to the washing water.

Perfume stains

A mixture of baking soda and ammonia provides the answer to removing nasty perfume stains. Make a thick paste with these ingredients, and smear it over the stain. Once you've done so, wait for it to dry – place it in the sun, if this is practical. Once it is dry, wash it as you normally would.

Rust stains

Soak the affected area with white distilled vinegar, then rub salt into the stain. Allow to dry, then wash in the normal way.

Salt stains on shoes in winter

A solution of 1 part white distilled vinegar with 1 part clean water will remove salt stains from shoes and boots.

Sauce stains

Stained cotton, cotton polyester and permanent press fabrics can be saved if they are sponged with white distilled vinegar within 24 hours and washed immediately.

Smoke stains

Smoke stains, whether yellow from cigarette fumes or black from the soot out of a fireplace, are another annoyance that baking soda can easily eliminate. Sprinkle the soda onto a damp cloth, and wipe away the deposits. Remember not to scrub too hard so as to avoid damaging paint; non-washable paint may still run.

Suede cleaner

To remove accidental grease spots on suede, dip a toothbrush in white distilled vinegar and gently brush over the area.

Tar stains on clothing

To get rid of tar deposits on clothing, a thick paste of baking soda in water will provide the answer. Let it soak in for a while, and then wash the piece of clothing using baking soda in place of washing powder. As if by magic, the tar will be gone.

Tea and coffee stains

Soak china and glassware in hot vinegar, and then wash in the normal way. For stubborn stains on cups and pots, add a teaspoon of salt to a little of the hot vinegar and rub onto the stain.

Vomit stains

If your baby is sick on their clothes (or most likely yours) after feeding, moisten a cloth, dip it in baking soda and dab at the fabric. The odour will disappear. Soak stained clothes in salt water before washing.

Wine stains

First of all, when the stain happens, sprinkle the area with baking soda. As soon as you get a chance, stretch the cloth tightly over a pan and pour boiling water over the baking soda covering the stain. The soda, and the stain, should dissolve straight out. If you haven't any baking soda handy, cover wine-stain with salt leaving it until the stain has lifted; rinse in cool water later.

Woodwork – stubborn water rings

- Hard to remove rings resulting from wet cups and glasses being placed on wood furniture may be removed by gently rubbing with a mixture of equal parts of white distilled vinegar and olive oil. Rub with the grain, and polish for the best results.

- Baking soda can also help to remove the ring-stains left behind by hot mugs and other heat sources on some finishes. Rub the stain gently with a soft cloth, in a circular motion, with a mixture made from equal amounts of baking soda and toothpaste. Clean up afterwards with furniture polish if there is residue that needs to be removed.

- Water spots on plain wooden boards or floors can often be removed with the aid of a damp cloth dipped into baking soda. Remember of course that you shouldn't over-soak wood because of the possible stains when it dries.

The Bathroom

Often a source of trouble and odours, the bathroom is a great place for putting to work salt, vinegar and baking soda.

Bathroom air freshener

The air of the room can be simply freshened by spiking some holes in the top of a box of baking soda and tucking it behind the toilet. Remember to change it every 3 months, so as to keep the deodorising power at maximum. Alternatively, you can simply pour some into a pretty dish and leave it on top of, or next to, the toilet cistern. If you like a pleasant scent in the bathroom, then try mixing baking soda with perfumed bath salts to make an attractive air freshener that deodorises unpleasant smells and replaces them with nice ones.

Bathroom all purpose cleaners

One of the most convenient ways to have it handy for use is to make up a squeeze-bottle solution ready for when you want it.

You can make a powerful bathroom cleanser from 6 tablespoons of baking soda, ½ cup of white distilled vinegar, and 4 cups of warm water. Mix this together thoroughly, and then store it in a handy spray bottle, ready for when you want to wipe down your bathroom surfaces.

An alternative for a thicker cleaner is to put 500 grams of baking soda into a bowl. Add a cup of warm water, and 4 tablespoons of washing up liquid. Blend this well together until you have a thick, creamy mixture, and then store it in an empty squeezable cleaner bottle. It's great for tough deposits.

Baths and sinks

❑   Old baths and sinks can be a real trial to get sparkling clean. A paste made with baking soda and white distilled vinegar makes a great cleaner. Apply it to the surface, leave it to sit and work for a short while, and then simply rub it off.

❑ If your bath has no-skid rubber strips, you'll know that sometimes they can really pong. The best way to clean these is to rinse them thoroughly with water and sprinkle them generously with baking soda. Let it sit for a while, then give the mat a quick scrub before rinsing it off.

❑ If you have a fibreglass bath, soak a sponge in white distilled vinegar and sprinkle it with baking soda. Use this to wipe the bath clean: it will take almost no effort. Remember to rinse well afterwards to clean off the vinegar. In fact, you can add 2 tablespoons of baking soda to your bathwater as you run it. Not only will it stop any grimy encrustations forming, but it will soften the water beautifully so you make the most of your bath soap.

Brushes

Combs and hair brushes can be kept sparkling clean by washing them in a solution of 1 tablespoon of baking soda and a litre of warm, clean water. Brushes must be rinsed thoroughly after washing with clean water and then dried.

Grouting

For the grouting between the tiles in the bathroom, make a paste of baking soda and water, and scrub with an old toothbrush. If there are heavy mould deposit problems, you can add a little bleach to the paste. Remember that you should never mix bleach with ammonia, as the resulting mixture can give off poisonous gases.

Marble surfaces

If you have marble to get clean, a simple paste of baking soda and vinegar makes a wonderful scrub for bringing back the shine.

Showers

- ❑ If you have a shower rather than a bath, vinegar and baking soda is still there to help you out. Use a spray using equal amounts of white distilled vinegar and water to remove mildew and mould from shower curtains. When taking the curtains down for washing, soak them in warm soapy water and 1 tablespoon of baking soda to clean them.
- ❑ When cleaning a fibreglass shower booth, use a damp sponge sprinkled with baking soda. It won't scratch, but most stains and deposits will lift straight off. Once you've wiped it down, a quick rinse and wipe dry is all that is needed.
- ❑ When the shower becomes just a dribble it's time to clean the shower rose. Dismantle the showerhead. Soak the pieces in a basin of white distilled vinegar and ½ cup of baking soda for 2 to 3 hours. Clean off any sediment with a stiff brush.
- ❑ To clean off glass shower doors, start by using a misting spray filled with white distilled vinegar to spray onto the door. Leave it for a minute or two to soak in a bit, and then wipe it down with a sponge onto which you have sprinkled baking soda. Rinse and wipe dry afterwards.

Sponges

A slimy sponge can be brought back to its new condition by soaking the sponge in 1 tablespoon of vinegar mixed with ½ litre of water for 1 hour. Rinse thoroughly afterwards.

Tiles

If the base of your shower booth is tiled, then dampen the surface and sprinkle baking soda onto it. Let it sit for a while, and then squeeze some plain shampoo onto a sponge. Use this to wipe the tiles over, and once you've finished, give it a quick rinse to get rid of the suds. It doesn't take long, and the results are great.

To clean away hard water deposits on wall tiles in a shower booth, rub the surface with undiluted white distilled vinegar. Leave for 15 minutes, then rinse thoroughly. Repeat if necessary.

Toilet bowls

- To keep your toilet bowl clean and fresh, scatter baking soda all around the bowl and into the pipe and scrub it vigorously with a clean toilet brush. Leave it for 10 minutes to stand before flushing, so as to make sure that all the calcium deposits from the water are washed away.
- When scale builds up in the toilet bowl, bale out the water to below the line of the deposit. Make up a mixture of domestic borax and white distilled vinegar in equal quantities. Spread the mixture on the deposits and leave for 2 to 3 hours. Brush off the sediment with a stiff brush. Treat all hard water deposits on bathroom fittings as necessary.
- A badly stained toilet bowl can be made to look like new. The bowl may be cleaned by adding 3 cupfuls of white distilled vinegar and 3 tablespoons of washing soda together in the bowl. Allow it to remain for a half hour, then give it a good brushing.
- Stubborn stains can be wiped off by using a thick, frothing paste of baking soda and white distilled vinegar. Spread it over the stains and scrub them away with a brush.

Doing the Laundry

You should note, when using vinegar in your laundry, that it can discolour some dyes and fabrics, so make sure that you test it on a small, inconspicuous area first.

Blankets

If your blankets get damp, getting rid of the smell can be difficult, unless you have baking soda close to hand. Sprinkle it on, and roll up the blankets. Leave for a day before shaking the baking soda out.

Clothes pre-wash cleaners

❑ To loosen up grime and dirt on clothing, make a thick paste of baking soda and water and rub it into the affected area. Let it sit for a while before putting the item into the wash. It is always a good idea with any anti-stain remedy to make sure that the clothing is not discoloured by first trying a small amount on an unobtrusive patch. Providing it doesn't discolour, the remedy will be safe to use.

❑ A similar procedure will help to loosen caked-on grime around the collar after a hard day. Rub some baking soda paste into the dirty area, and leave it to soak in for a bit. Just before you put the shirt or blouse into the wash, rub a little white distilled vinegar over the paste for a deep-cleansing fizzing action. This technique will also shift sweat stains and lingering odour patches.

❑ If there is a problem with an acid spill (such as drain-unblocking fluids, battery acid, vomit and urine, and dark-room film developer) on clothing, the first thing to do is to flush the area with cold water. Follow this up by scattering baking soda over the patch and allowing it to sit for a while before washing. If the acid has dried in, then rub baking soda paste in before washing, so that the water does not activate the acid again.

Clothes rinse

Clothes will rinse cleaner if a cup of white distilled vinegar is added to the last rinse water. The acid in this vinegar solution will be too mild to harm the fabrics but strong enough to dissolve the alkali in soaps and detergents.

Clothes softener

Baking soda can be used instead of clothing softeners or conditioners where sensitive skin is a problem, and it is great for soaking the chlorine out of swimming costumes: make a weak solution of baking soda in water, and use this to rinse all the chemicals straight out. Baking soda is non-antagonistic to the skin, and so is extremely suitable for people who have a problem with chemicals or other irritants.

Fabric colour fixer

To stop colours from running on their first wash, immerse them in full strength white distilled vinegar before washing.

Face flannels

Slimy face flannels can be revitalised by boiling in a weak solution of vinegar and water. One teaspoon of white distilled vinegar to half a litre of water is enough.

Hem tidy

Remove unsightly holes left in the fabric after a hem or seam has been altered by placing a cloth, moistened with white distilled vinegar, under the fabric and a damp cloth on the top and then iron.

Ironing

To prevent clothes becoming shiny when pressing with a hot iron, place over the garment a cloth that has been sprayed with a solution in the ratio of 1 part of white distilled vinegar to 2 parts of water.

Ironing out creases

To remove stubborn creases, sponge the material with white distilled vinegar and press with a warm iron.

Lint clinging to clothes

Add one cup white distilled vinegar to each wash load.

Mildew on curtains

Add 150 millilitres of lavender vinegar to the water when washing, and another cupful when rinsing.

Nappies

Soiled nappies should be soaked in a solution of cold water and a tablespoon of baking soda before washing in the usual way.

Nylon tights

When washing your nylon tights add 1 tablespoon of white distilled vinegar to the final rinse water to make them feel good and last longer.

Setting colours

When you are colour dyeing, add about a cupful of white distilled vinegar to the last rinse water to help set the colour.

Scorch marks

Lightly rub the scorched cloth with a lint-free cloth soaked in vinegar. If heavily marked, continue to rub lightly with a silver coin.

Sharper creases in trousers

For a sharper crease in trousers, turn the trousers inside out and dampen the creases with a cloth wrung out from a solution of ¼ cup of white distilled vinegar and 1 cup of water. Turn the trousers the right way round, place brown paper over the crease and press with a hot iron.

Sharper creases in knitwear

First dampen the garment with a cloth that has been rinsed in a solution of 2 parts of clean water to 1 part of white distilled vinegar. Cover the garment with brown paper and apply a hot iron.

Shiny patches when ironing

Get rid of shiny seats on trousers and skirts by soaking a cloth in a solution of 1 part white distilled vinegar to 4 parts water. Place this over the affected area and press the garment lightly.

Softer sheets

Add 1 cup of white distilled vinegar during the rinse cycle each time you wash your sheets. It will leave them soft and fresh.

Soft fluffy blankets

A cup of white distilled vinegar added to the wash will make a good rinse for both cotton and wool blankets. You will find that it leaves them free of soap odour and that their nap is soft and fluffy as new.

Soap remover

Eliminate excess froth when washing clothes by hand by adding a tablespoon of white distilled vinegar to the second rinse. Finally rinse in plain water to finish off.

Starch remover

Baking soda is great for removing the chemicals that are sprayed onto new clothes if you have sensitive skin. First soak the clothing in a solution of 2 cups of vinegar in ½ litre of water for two hours, then rinse it and soak it in a solution of 2 cups of baking soda in ½ litre of water for a further two hours. Put it through the wash as normal, and all the starches and fixatives should be removed. Remember, you must test an inconspicuous area of the fabric first.

Washing

☐ When it comes to the wash, you'll need to have your baking soda close at hand. It can be a great booster for the power of whiteners and bleaches. Rather than use a cup of bleach, use half a cup and half a cup of baking soda for the same whitening power. You'll cut down on chemicals, soften the impact on your clothes, reduce the amount of pollutant going down the drain, and save money into the bargain. For a special, delicate bleach for fragile fabrics, add equal amounts of baking soda and lemon juice together, and use it in the same way that you'd use your normal bleach. Remember to check the fabric for suitability first, of course.

☐ If you don't want to bleach but you still want extra cleaning power, add ½ cup of baking soda to the wash when you are using liquid detergents (powdered detergents won't be boosted by baking soda). You'll get brighter colours, whiter whites, and cleaner clothes. Baking soda added to the wash will also soften the water, making the detergent go further, remove the discolouration of age on clothing, soften your fabrics and flush out the smell of mothballs.

☐ When something such as a crayon or pen slips past your vigilant eye and into the machine, baking soda can help. Set the machine on the hottest wash that the fabrics can cope with, and add between ½ and all of a 450 gram box of baking soda over the clothes in the drum, depending on how bad the staining is. For particularly serious cases, you may need to repeat this.

☐ If you get nasty deposits left in the washing machine – chewing gum, for example – then put a handful of baking soda and water paste onto a plastic scouring pad and use this to lift the offending deposit from your machine.

Odour eaters

Basic bouquet

To make a room smelling clean and sweet, place a small bowl of white distilled vinegar in the warmest corner of the room. To make an even better scent to a room while at the same time removing an unpleasant odour, add cardamom or other fragrant spice to the bowl of white distilled vinegar.

Bread bin

When cleaning the bread bin, keep it smelling sweet by wiping it down with a cloth moistened in white distilled vinegar.

Carpets

To help your carpets stay smelling fresh, spread dry baking soda over them and leave it overnight to absorb ground-in smells. For thick carpets or strong smells, particularly if you have a cat or dog, you can brush the baking soda into the pile with a stiff broom. Once it has been allowed to stand for a few hours, you can vacuum it out to leave your carpets looking clean and smelling fresh. Alternatively, you can mix a few drops of your favourite perfume in with the baking soda before you spread it over the carpets, so that you leave a pleasant smell behind when you vacuum the mixture up the next day.

You can take the edge from the smell of a new carpet by putting down a layer of baking soda on the floor beneath the carpet just before it is laid. Don't do this on solid wooden floors though, as it will not be good for the wood.

Cat litter odours

Baking soda absorbs cat litter odours. Cover the bottom of the cat box with 1 part baking soda; then add a layer of 3 parts cat litter on top.

Cat odours

To eliminate any after odour, add 12 drops of lavender vinegar to a cup of baking soda, mixing well. If the scent is not strong enough, add more of the lavender vinegar, a drop at a time, until sufficiently scented. Sprinkle over the affected spot with a flour sifter, leave for 2 hours and then vacuum up.

Clothing

- Odours may be removed from clothing by hanging them over a bowl that has been filled with a kettleful of hot water and 1 cup of white distilled vinegar.
- Sprinkling a little baking soda into your socks in the morning makes a great way to cut down on foot odour.
- You can cut down on persistent shoe odour by sprinkling in a little baking soda after wearing them. Shake out any excess in the morning.
- Baking soda can stiffen up leather shoes, so you may not want to use it in that type of footwear. It will, however, loosen cotton laces that have become stiff with wear and dirt. Rub a little baking soda paste into the laces to make them softer and more manageable.

Cooking smells

To remove smells from the kitchen, boil a cup of water with 1 tablespoon of lavender vinegar added to it.

Drains

Boil 200 millilitres of vinegar and pour directly into the drain. Leave for 10 minutes before using the drain.

Remove odours from sink drainpipes with a daily treatment of strong, hot solution of salt water.

Fish smells on plates and utensils

Add a tablespoon of white distilled vinegar to the washing-up water. Rinse thoroughly in clean water before drying.

Fridges

Deodorise your fridge and freezer by putting in an open container of baking soda to absorb odours. Stir and turn over the soda from time to time. Replace every 2 months.

Glass bottles and jars

To remove the odours left by the former contents of old bottles and jars rinse them in white distilled vinegar, and then wash them in clean soapy water.

Hands

To remove strong odours from your hands, wet your hands and rub them hard with baking soda, then rinse.

Holdalls

If you are an active person, you can keep your sports holdall smell-free by putting a little baking soda in the bottom of it at night, and then shaking it out in the mornings. It'll help cut down on perspiration smells.

Laundry basket odours

You can also keep your pile of things to wash smelling pleasant in the same way; whenever you add clothes, also scatter some baking soda over them. When you are ready to wash them, just put them straight into the machine – there's no need to shake the soda out first.

Oil and petrol smells

The stench of oil, petrol, diesel and other fuels is a little trickier to get rid of. Baking soda is persistent though; put the clothes into a plastic bag, such as a bin liner, and cover them with a generous amount of baking soda. Tie the bag up, and leave it somewhere fairly warm for a few days before giving the clothes a wash.

Oven odours

Remove offensive odours from an oven with salt and cinnamon.

Pets

Remove odorous smells from pets by brushing their coat with white distilled vinegar.

Plastic food containers

Add a teaspoon of baking soda to hot water when washing food and drink containers. It will take away strong food smells as well as leaving the container clean for next time it is used.

Leave a slice of bread that has been sprinkled with white distilled vinegar in the lunchbox overnight. This will ensure that it smells clean and sweet when used next day.

Smoke odours

Smoke, from fire or cigarettes, is notorious for sticking in your clothing. The smell can be easily neutralised before washing by soaking the smoky clothes in a solution of a cup of baking soda in ½ litre of water.

Sports and work shoes

Banish the odour of sweat from footwear by sprinkling baking soda inside after use. Be sure to remove them from your holdall when you get home, and leave them where fresh air can get to them.

Vomit odour

One of the most lingering is the acidic smell left behind when someone has been sick. Rubbing plain baking soda into the patch will kill the scent and make it easy to wash out.

Pets

Bird bath

To keep the water in the birdbath sparkling clean, remove any debris and give the bath a good clean with 50/50 white distilled vinegar and water. Refill with fresh water.

Bird cages

Keep your pets healthy by wiping the bars and surfaces with a solution of 50/50 white distilled vinegar and hot water.

Cat deterrent

Prevent cats from fouling the children's sand box by spraying white distilled vinegar round the perimeter of the box whenever the box is in use.

To keep cats out of the garden sprinkle any kind of vinegar on areas you don't want the cat walking, sleeping, or scratching on.

Dog and cat markers

Territorial claims around doorways should be washed thoroughly with warm soapy water, then liberally wiped over with the following disinfectant: dissolve 40 drops of lavender vinegar in 10 millilitres of methylated spirits, and blend with a litre of tepid water. Use the disinfectant immediately, wiping liberally over the affected area.

Dog scratching deterrent

To stop your dog from scratching his ears, wipe his ears with a clean cloth dipped in a solution of half water and half white distilled vinegar. If he persists in scratching he should be taken to the vet for an examination.

Dog spray

Keep a spray bottle containing half white distilled vinegar and half water for when your dog misbehaves. He will learn to have respect for the spray and will do as he is told.

Dog puddles

For urine stains, mop up quickly to prevent as much urine as possible from soaking into the carpet, then sponge with the following solution: dissolve 1 tablespoon of ammonia with 1 cupful of warm water. Normally urine is acidic, however, if this mixture is not successful the urine could be alkaline and should be sponged with equal quantities of white distilled vinegar and warm water.

Sprinkle white distilled vinegar over the area soiled. Wait a few minutes and then sponge from the centre outwards. Blot up excess liquid with a dry cloth. Repeat this procedure for stubborn stains. *(Always make sure that the carpet is colour fast before attempting to use liquids for cleaning.)*

Drinking water

Add half a teaspoon of white distilled vinegar to your pet's drinking water to eliminate body odour and encourage shiny fur.

Add a few drops of apple cider vinegar to the water in the chicken run to deter them from pecking at each other.

Ear cleanser for pets

Mix 1 part rubbing alcohol with 1 part white distilled vinegar and 1 part distilled water. Store it in a clean dropper bottle and use it to clean out your pets' ears. Just squirt 8-10 drops in each ear holding the head to one side; let it stand in ear for a minute then massage the ear around in a circle. Tilt and wipe out with paper tissue. Apply once a month or if they are ear scratching apply daily for 3 days. If they continue scratching or rubbing their ears, consult your vet.

Horses

To deter flies from biting in hot weather, rinse out a cloth in 50/50 white distilled vinegar and water and wipe your horse's vulnerable parts.

Add approximately 5 teaspoons of apple cider vinegar to your horse's oats morning and evening to dramatically reduce fly bites.

Add a tablespoon of apple cider vinegar to a litre of drinking water. It helps to deal with heat stress. Also helps to repel mosquitoes.

Parrot diet

Add a few drops of apple cider vinegar to your parrot's mash diet as a condiment just as you would add salad dressing to a salad. Some avian health practitioners recommend that apple cider vinegar be placed in the bird's fresh food. The dosage is ¼ teaspoon for small parrots and ½ teaspoon for medium-large parrots. It can also be given orally, diluted in water under the guidance of a vet or avian health practitioner.

Apple cider vinegar has been used successfully for dry, itchy or infected skin and feather problems.

Pet hair

To remove pet hair from carpet or furniture: mix 1 part fabric softener to 3 parts white distilled vinegar in spray bottle and spray on carpets and furniture. Wait 2 or more hours, then vacuum. Hair will pick up much easier.

Rabbit hutch cleanser

When cleaning the litter tray in a rabbit hutch, use neat white distilled vinegar; it keeps the litter boxes like new. If there is already a build-up of dried urine in the box, scrubbing with white distilled vinegar will get rid of it.

Gardening

Aphid and whitefly spray

Mix 1 teaspoon of baking soda in with a third of a cup of vegetable oil, and then add 2 teaspoons of this combination to your water sprayer for each cup of water. It will finish off the undesirable pests.

Azaleas and rhododendrons

Occasionally water plants with a mixture of 2 tablespoons white distilled vinegar to a litre of water.

Codling moths

To catch codling moths, use a mixture of 2 parts white distilled vinegar and one part black treacle. Place this mixture in a tin and hang it in the apple tree. Clean out the moths and place more mixture in the tin when needed.

Fish bowl cleaner

Small fish bowls and fish tanks can be kept clean by rubbing the glass with a cloth dipped in white distilled vinegar. Make sure the bowl or tank is thoroughly rinsed out before retuning the fish.

Flowerpot cleaner

Instead of throwing away old flowerpots just place them in a bucket of cold water and add a cupful of white distilled vinegar. Soak the pots for an hour, or until they look clean and new.

Deter slugs and snails from eating your pot plants by wiping the rim of the pot with full strength white distilled vinegar each evening whilst the plants are vulnerable.

Fly catcher

To catch flies, place a piece of meat in a jar. Using a 2 litre jar, place a small piece of meat covered in fruit vinegar into the jar. Punch a few holes big enough for the flies to crawl in, into the lid of the jar. Screw on the lid and set in a good fly location. When the fly crawls in, it can't get out. Clean out the jar when the smell gets to strong or it gets full of flies.

Garden shed sanitiser

Deter insects from making your shed their home with a weekly spray of full strength white distilled vinegar on all the surfaces and corners.

Garden spray

Baking soda can be used to make an excellent spray against black spot, powdery mildew and other similar plant diseases. Put 7 tablespoons of soda into a 20 litre drum of water, and add a few drops of insecticide, but make sure that it is a formulation that does not contain pyrethrums. Spray every other day to combat the disease. Keep an eye out for signs of damage after a week or so; if there aren't any, you can keep up the treatment once a week all through the season.

Grass killer

Kill off grass that is growing on paths and driveways by pouring white distilled vinegar on it.

Greenhouse sanitiser

After the garden greenhouse has been cleaned out at the end of the season, give everything a good spray with full strength white distilled vinegar.

Slug spray

Get rid of slugs with a mix of 1 part white distilled vinegar and 1 part water. Mix vinegar and water in a spray bottle and spray directly onto the slug. They will die almost immediately. Also spray the ground around your plants and any hidden slugs will come out of the sprayed soil and die.

Weed killer

To kill weeds in areas that you don't plan to plant anything you can use a solution of 1 tablespoon white distilled vinegar and 2 tablespoons of salt with 1 litre of water. Spray the weed until soaked.

D.I.Y.

Brushes

Treat brushes that have hardened dirt or paint on them by boiling them in undiluted white distilled vinegar. Leave them to soak for 1 hour. Then wash off the dirt and paint with hot soapy water.

Car battery maintenance

When the terminals on your car battery start to corrode and deposits of white powder start to build up, make up a thick baking soda paste to apply to the affected areas. Brush them clean afterwards, and apply a protective layer of grease or petroleum jelly to help prevent further corrosion. Remember not to touch both terminals simultaneously so as to avoid any chance of a shock.

Car seats and mats

Rinse down vinyl seats with a baking soda solution to keep them free of odours, or sprinkle dry baking soda onto fabric seats and leave it for half an hour before vacuuming or brushing it off. You can combat general smells by sprinkling baking soda beneath the foot mats in the car, and if you have a compartment for a dog or other pet to ride in, you can also sprinkle this with baking soda on a regular basis to help neutralise the odour.

Cracks and holes in walls

Cracks and holes in white walls can also be healed up with baking soda. Make a thick paste with water, and use it to fill the crack. When it dries, it blends in well with plaster. To make it permanent, mix the baking soda with a suitable white glue. Remember not to use superglues; they dry too fast, and they bond skin and eyes in seconds. If you are a dab hand at mixing colours, then adding the right mix of oil paints to the blend can provide you with a handy patching mixture that matches your wall closely – but remember that many paints change colour slightly as they dry, so be careful.

Drains

Keep your drains clean and free flowing by putting 4 tablespoons of soda in them each week. Flush the soda down with hot water.

When a drain is blocked, make up a solution of 200 millilitres vinegar with 75 grams of baking soda. Pour directly into the drain. Leave for 10 minutes. Then run clean hot water down the drain to clear the grease and debris.

Fire prevention

Be sure to keep an extra box of baking soda by your electric cooker in case of grease or electrical fire. Scatter the powder by the handful to safely put it out.

Keep a container of baking soda in your garage as well as in your car to put out a fire. It won't damage anything it touches.

Baking soda will also put out fires in clothing, fuel, wood, upholstery and rugs.

Floorboard cleaner

Before waxing stripped floorboards clean the floor with a mixture of 1 part of white distilled vinegar to 3 parts of water. It neutralises the chemicals and makes wax or floor finishes adhere better.

Frost free windscreen

White distilled vinegar will help to keep frost off the windscreen. Use a solution of 3 parts white distilled vinegar to 1 part of water. Wipe the solution over the windscreen before the frost has a chance to freeze the glass.

Galvanised metal

Paint adheres better to galvanised metal that has been wiped with white distilled vinegar.

Garage floors

Sprinkle baking soda on a greasy garage floor surface, let it stand, then scrub and rinse.

Glue

Vinegar makes excellent glue for fabric and leather goods. Take 1 sachet clear gelatine, 3 tablespoons of white distilled vinegar, 3 tablespoons of water, and 1 teaspoon of glycerine. Melt the gelatine in water on a low heat, then add the other ingredients and mix well. Apply the glue whilst it is still warm. Store the remaining glue in a small plastic or glass jar. Warm it up next time before use.

Many glues may be dissolved by applying a coating of white distilled vinegar and letting it soak for a while.

Grout cleaner

To clean grout spray white distilled vinegar over the tiles, wait 5 minutes, then scrub with a toothbrush.

Loosen glued joints

To loosen old glue around rungs and joints of tables and chairs under repair, apply white distilled vinegar to the joints with a small oilcan.

Paint on windows

Rub the paint with hot undiluted vinegar to soften it. Remove the paint and clean the glass in the normal way.

Paintwork

When you are dealing with paintwork, baking soda on a wet sponge will get rid of most marks from washable paint. This includes crayon, pencil and markers, if you have decoratively-minded children, as well as grease marks. Remember to scrub painted walls gently, so as not to cut through the paint. Crayon can, in fact, be removed from most surfaces using the same procedure, including radiators, hearths and doors.

Retard patching plaster from drying

Add 1 tablespoon white distilled vinegar to the water when mixing plaster to slow the drying time.

Rust cutter

Loosen rusted or corroded bolts and hinges by soaking in white distilled vinegar.

Scratched tabletops

If a beeswax-polished surface becomes scratched or spotted, rub the scratches or spots with white vinegar and polish again with beeswax whilst the surface is still wet.

Septic tank maintenance

If you have a septic tank, then it is well worth flushing 2 cups of baking soda straight down the toilet once a week. It will help to keep the acid levels down, helping to prevent blockages, clumping and the corrosive gases which can attack both concrete and metal tanks. It may also go some small way to keeping the odour of the tank a little less unpleasant in the worst-case scenario of an overflow or leak, although obviously it will have its work cut out!

Wallpaper remover

Mix equal parts white distilled vinegar and hot water. Use a paint roller to wet the walls with the solution. The paper should come off quite easily.

Wood panelling cleaner

Wood panelling on walls that has been neglected may be cleaned with a mixture of 1 part of olive oil to 2 parts of white distilled vinegar in 50 parts of warm water. Rinse a soft cloth in the solution and wipe the panelling clean. Finally, dry with a soft, dry cloth.

Woodstain

To tint wood with a colourful shiny sheen, Mix a sufficient amount of white distilled vinegar with your chosen colour of water-based ink until it is the colour you require. Apply to the wood with a brush or rag. Wipe off excess and let dry.

Wood varnish restoration

Varnished wooden tops often become cloudy in appearance due to water being spilt on them. To restore the original sheen, rub the wood with a soft cloth rinsed in a solution of 1 tablespoon of white distilled vinegar diluted in a litre of water. Complete the job by wiping the surface with a soft dry cloth.

Woodwork – general cleaner

Removed dirt and grime from woodwork with a solution of 1 cupful of ammonia, ½ a cupful of white distilled vinegar, and ¼ cupful of washing soda, and a cupful of warm water. Mix the solution in a large bowl, then use a soft cloth rinsed in the solution.

Interests and Hobbies

Barbecue tools

Clean your spatulas etc., with a spray of white distilled vinegar during use to remove uncooked food from them when serving cooked food.

Caravanning

Give the caravan a good spray and clean up with spray of white distilled vinegar before settling in. It will stand you in good stead, and you will enjoy your holiday all the more.

Camping

If you enjoy camping, then baking soda can be a great help to freshen sleeping bags and tents. Scatter some evenly inside them when you roll them up to put them away, and then shake it out when you next unroll them for use. They'll be far sweeter and more inviting for it.

Coin collecting

If you are a collector, baking soda can help in a number of ways. It is great for cleaning up old coins. Make a paste of soda with water and scrub. Where corrosion is bad, soaking in a strong baking soda solution can lift off all sorts of deposits. You should seek professional advice before using this method to clean a valuable coin, of course. Paper products, such as old bank notes, books, stamps and so on can be freed from mildew and damp smells by sprinkling with baking soda and leaving for a few days.

Fisherman's lures

If you plan to do some fishing, you can add baking soda to certain types of ventilated lures and the reaction will make them jump and spin in the water, attracting the attention of big fish in the area.

Fly and insect repellent

Take a spray bottle filled with white distilled vinegar and spray round the vicinity of your picnic or barbecue to deter flies and insects.

Hiking and rambling

Take a small bottle spray filled with white distilled vinegar for spraying midges and persistent biting insects.

Musical instruments

Baking soda also makes a great cleanser for the mouthpieces of musical instruments when used as a solution with water to bathe the pieces in. Remember to rinse and allow to dry before reassembly.

Party tricks

For a really impressive baking soda trick make a volcano. Bury a small, wide-necked bottle (such as a baby food jar) containing 4 teaspoons of baking soda inside a conical mound of sand. Make sure that you do not push the sand into the neck of the bottle, and that you leave a hole at the top leading to the bottle. In another jar, mix together ½ a cup of water, ¼ of a cup of washing up liquid, ¼ of a cup of vinegar, and a generous dash of cochineal red food colouring. When you pour some of this mixture into the bottle at the bottom of the mound of sand, the vinegar and baking soda will react and bubbles will form, frothing up and out of the cone of sand like an erupting volcano. To make your own life easier, keep all of this firmly inside a plastic tray, so that you don't stain the carpets or table. You can also experiment with the temperature of the vinegar and water mix to see how the heat produces different speeds of reaction. Chill it down in the fridge for a slow, inexorable rise, or heat it in a microwave for a thrillingly fast reaction.

Another great trick is to fill a clear plastic or glass container with water, and add 3 teaspoons of baking soda and a ¼ cup of vinegar. Leave this for a moment to start reacting, and then put some light items into the container. Buttons and little pieces of raw pasta are both suitable. The items will sink initially, but they will then begin to rise as the bubbles from the reaction form on the surface and cling to provide lift. When the object reaches the top, the bubbles break again and the item sinks once more, beginning the process all over again. Keep the reaction freshened up by adding vinegar and baking soda in the ratio of 3 parts to 1 respectively.

Sanitiser

Use your spray bottle of white distilled vinegar to sanitise eating utensils and surfaces for eating.

Sewing

When you want to clean pins, needles and knitting needles, make a small pin-cushion stuffed with baking soda and push the needles through the bag several times, until they are clean.

If you are sewing pillows, cushions or something with a filling, sprinkle baking soda in before you sew it up to help keep the object smelling fresh and clean.

Part Two

Health and Hygiene

SALT, VINEGAR, cayenne pepper and baking soda are all great around the home, but they also have a huge number of handy applications for smoothing the bumps and aches out of everyday life for you and your family.

Remember that you should always seek medical advice before using any home remedy, and people on low sodium diets, with high blood pressure or pregnant women should consult their doctor before using salt or baking soda.

Arteries – clogged

Modern medicine has achieved notable success in discovering the causes of atherosclerosis and related cardiovascular ailments. The best 'treatment' is not to let your arteries get clogged in the first place. Some advocates of apple cider vinegar say that a drink of 1 tablespoon of apple cider vinegar in a glass of fresh water every day will help to reduce clogged arteries. However, there are no scientific research papers to back up this claim. Since apple cider vinegar will do no harm, it is certainly worth trying.

Aspirin

Some people find that the common household painkiller, aspirin, gives them indigestion. This can be countered by adding half a teaspoon of baking soda to the water you use to swallow the pills with.

Acne

Make up a solution of 2 tablespoons of white distilled vinegar, the juice of 1 garlic clove, and 1 cup of boiled, cooled water. Dab the solution on the affected area several times a day. Always wash the skin before applying.

Alternatively, slice a clove of garlic in half. Hold the halved clove on the affected area for a few minutes. Repeat as often as necessary.

Antiseptic wash

Use a good quality white distilled vinegar for all-round use in the bathroom and toilet.

Anxiety attacks

Anxiety is often confused with fear of the unknown. What's more, it can make you stay up all night worrying. To help overcome the problem, try meditation. It cultivates a calmness that eases that anxious feeling. Fill a small glass bowl with lavender vinegar and place it on a side table so that the fragrance can fill the air whilst you are meditating.

Arthritis

To relief painful joints, add 1 to 4 cupfuls of apple cider vinegar to hot bath water. The amount of apple cider vinegar depends on how much water you use for your bath, but for an average size bath, use 2 cupfuls. Soak for as long as you like; it will make you feel better all over. Be careful not to get the water in your eyes when you add larger quantities, as it will cause your eyes to sting for a while.

Some help may be obtained by drinking half a glassful of water mixed with a teaspoon of apple cider vinegar before meals. Some people may prefer to do this every other day without any loss of benefit.

A mixture of warm honey, whiskey and apple cider vinegar is an old time remedy for arthritic bones.

To bring quick relief, massage the affected parts with the cayenne oil or cayenne liniment. *(See Cayenne oil and Liniment)*

Asthma

Take 1 tablespoon of apple cider vinegar in a glass of water should be taken in sips for half an hour. After a further half an hour has elapsed the treatment should be repeated. The wheezing should lessen in intensity quite considerably. However, should wheezing still persist a second glass of the same mixture should be taken. Deep breathing exercises are also a beneficial treatment.

Athlete's foot

Bathe the afflicted area with a cotton-wool pad soaked in apple cider vinegar and rub with a cut clove of garlic. Rinse your feet in clean warm water and your problem should go within a week.

Alternatively, crush a clove of garlic and mix with a small amount of petroleum jelly. Apply the ointment to the infected area with a cotton-wool swab. Hold the swab in place with an adhesive plaster if necessary. Leave in place for thirty minutes, and then remove. Always use a clean cotton-wool swab for each foot and for each application.

You can also use baking soda to combat fungal infections such as athlete's foot. Make a thick paste of the powder with water, and smear it on between your toes. Leave it for ¼ an hour before rinsing off. Do this twice a day to bring athlete's foot under control. You can help the process by adding a sprinkling of baking soda to socks and shoes. This will help decrease moisture levels, making the environment healthier for you and less pleasant for the fungus.

Bladder infections

One time when it is recommended that you follow the maximum

permitted dose for a while is when you want to clear up bladder infections. The maximum dosage is ½ teaspoon of baking soda to half a glass of water every two hours, with no more than 8 in any one 24 hour period. Taking a maximum dose of baking soda for 3 days can help to clear up a range of bacteriological bladder problems by changing the acidity levels of your urine, and so of the bladder cavity. If infections are making urination painful or causing inflamed skin, baking soda can help again. Add 3 tablespoons of it to your bath water to help bring relief.

Bites, rashes and stings

Apply soda directly to insect bites, rashes and poison ivy to relieve discomfort. Make a paste with water.

If you have been stung by a jellyfish, or by any other sea creature that stings, wash off the remaining pieces of tentacles with seawater as quickly as possible. On no account try to pick them off, as this action will only serve to squeeze more venom out of them. To reduce the pain and swelling, use any kind of vinegar that is immediately available, even that from the local seaside fish-and-chip shop. It is also a good idea to consult a doctor as soon as possible.

Bee stings can be dealt with quickly if you remove the stinger and venom sac from your skin to prevent more venom being injected into the wound. The best way to remove the stinger and sac is to use the back of your thumbnail. Scrape along your skin with your nail, getting underneath the barb, then flick it out. On no account squeeze the venom sac whilst doing this, as it will inject more venom into the wound.

To obtain relief, apply a paste made with baking soda and apple cider vinegar to the site of the sting. The soda helps to ease the pain, and the vinegar breaks down the proteins in the sting.

For wasp stings use lemon juice or dilute vinegar, because their stings are not acidic.

Bleeding cuts and scrapes (minor)

If a cut doesn't stop bleeding immediately, wash the wound with a very weak solution of apple cider vinegar and clean water.

Stop a cut from bleeding by sprinkling cayenne pepper into the cut. It should stop immediately.

You can also use baking soda to clean out narrow cuts and grazes. Make a thick paste of baking soda and water, and work it into the wound, before rinsing it out, and the dirt with it. You can repeat as many times as is necessary to get the cut really clean.

Blocked nose

When using steam to clear a blocked nose, add a teaspoon of white distilled vinegar to the water.

Bunions

Reduce the pain of bunions by rubbing in a mixture of ¼ teaspoon of cayenne pepper and ½ teaspoon of baby oil.

Burns – minor

If you are unlucky enough to get burnt, baking soda can help yet again. Add some baking soda to a jug of ice water and use this mixture to dip a towel into, which should then be held against the burn. Refresh the towel frequently to keep it as cold as possible. Keep applying the mixture until there is no heat left in the burnt area. The baking soda will help to stop your skin from blistering painfully.

Baking soda is just as good against acid burns. If you do get splashed with acid, run the area under cold water immediately and then neutralise the acid by sprinkling baking soda over the area.

Candida albicans

When your body has trouble with a thrush infection, take a sitz bath. Fill the bath to hip level with warm water and then add 100 millilitres of apple cider vinegar. Allow the lower half of your body to get a good soaking: in this way, you will help to rectify the alkalinity of your vaginal pH.

Cayenne oil – home made

Most analgesic creams, liniments and lotions available commercially today contain capsaicin as their main active ingredient. Applying any product that contains capsaicin extracted from cayenne pepper will first of all stimulate or cause the skin to glow fiery red (due to the irritation of mucous membrane) and subsequently, will decrease the intensity of visceral pain in the area of where the product was applied.

Home-made cayenne oil could be prepared by infusing 25 grams of cayenne pepper in 500 millilitres of olive oil for about 10 to 14 days. The oil is warmed daily under a very low heat. Other rubefacient herbs such as cloves, mustard, ginger and black pepper could be added if desired.

Cayenne liniment – home made

A liniment is usually prepared by steeping rubefacient herbs like cayenne into 70 per cent alcohol for about 10 to 14 days. After filtering, the liniment is then bottled and labelled and is ready for external use. The cayenne oil prepared as indicated above could be added to the liniment to double or to enhance its efficacy. This home-made cayenne pepper liniment is superior to the cayenne oil because it absorbs easily through the skin when it is applied externally.

Circulation – blood

Use cayenne pepper liberally on your cooked vegetables and meats. It helps to thin the blood, and prevents clotting.

Cold chills

Put a tablespoon of apple cider vinegar seasoned with salt and pepper in a cup of warm water, and drink. Alternate this drink every two hours with a cup of strong willow bark tea. Dogwood will do if water-willow cannot be obtained.

Cold sores

A virus, usually on the outside of your lips or mouth, causes cold sores. Often it lingers for a week or two and then eases. The direct method of treatment is to dab the affected area with gauze soaked in diluted white vinegar or witch hazel. It will help to dry out the sore, and will probably sting whilst doing so.

Colds and flu

- A delicious recipe for a cold or flu! Cut up 6 cloves of garlic and sauté in olive oil, being careful not to let them burn. Add a litre of stock (such as beef), and let it come to a boil for just a few moments. Then lower the heat. Separate two eggs and add the whites to the hot liquid, stirring rapidly. Mix the yolks with two tablespoons of apple cider vinegar and then pour them in. Add salt and pepper if you want and some croutons, if handy.
- To ward off a cold, sore throat, or at the onset of flu, sip 1 cup of cayenne tea 3 times a day as a preventative measure.
- A tablespoon of apple cider vinegar and a teaspoon of honey helps relieve chest congestion after a cold. You can also heat it with a touch of whiskey and to help heal cold and flu symptoms.
- You can use a commercial cough medicine to suppress your cough, but what you really need to do is get rid of the phlegm. You'll be better off by mixing together 1 tablespoon of honey, 1 dessertspoonful of apple cider vinegar, and the oil

from a full strength garlic capsule. Take 1 teaspoon before meals and before going to bed at night.

❑ Or, to help bring fast relief to a tickly cough, make up a mixture of 1 part apple cider vinegar to 2 parts of honey. Take a teaspoon of the mixture whenever the cough begins to irritate. Shake the bottle well, before taking.

❑ To prevent daytime coughing, take 2 teaspoons of apple cider vinegar and 2 of honey mixed with a glassful of water before meals, or when the irritation occurs. In the evening it would be an idea to have this mixture by your side so that it can be sipped during the evening if an attack presents itself.

❑ Baking soda can also help with a congested chest, providing your vaporiser can accept additives. If it can, just add a teaspoon of baking soda to the contents, and it will help provide extra chest-clearing action.

❑ When placed over the chest region, a cayenne pepper poultice *(See Poultice)* helps in the treatment of chest and lung congestion. A cup of tea made from plantain, sage, thyme, nettle, chickweed, etc. could be taken daily. Up to two to three of these herbs could be combined and used for the tea. This remedy will also relieve chest pain and mucous congestion along the entire respiratory tract.

❑ In some rural part of West Africa, a spoonful of cayenne pepper is burnt like an incense within the home – as a preventive measure against flu, internal and external cold and some catarrhal conditions associated with the changes in weather.

Colitis

Take a dose of 2 teaspoons apple cider vinegar and a teaspoon of honey with water, three times a day. An enema of a teaspoon or more of molasses is also very helpful.

Constipation (adults)

Take a glass of hot water with 1 teaspoon honey and 1 teaspoon apple cider vinegar first thing in the morning.

Corns and calluses

Corns and calluses require the attention of a podiatrist if they are very painful. Lotions and bath oils containing lanolin or glycerine may help, or you can buy plasters to soften the impact when walking on hard surfaces. A folk remedy lays claim to success by making a paste with 1 teaspoon of vinegar and enough wholemeal flour to bind the ingredients together. Place on the corn and cover with a slice of onion. Wrap a bandage round the foot and leave in place overnight.

Tape 2 pieces of stale bread soaked in apple cider vinegar over the corn. The next morning your skin will be like new.

Diarrhoea

Due to its healing properties, diarrhoea can be controlled in a very short time, (that is unless some serious physical disorder is apparent). Take one teaspoon of apple cider vinegar in a glass of water before and between meals i.e. approximately six glasses during the course of the day. It should be noted, however, that diarrhoea is a natural attempt on the part of the body to eliminate some poison which is irritating the digestive tract. On no account should any drugs be taken to suppress these healing symptoms – on the other hand the cider vinegar will lessen the intensity, but will allow the natural course of elimination to take place.

Dizziness

Two teaspoons of apple cider vinegar together with 2 teaspoons of honey in a glass of hot or cold water three times a day should help this annoying occurrence quite considerably. However, one should never expect instant results, as nature works slowly, though effectively. You will notice a lessened intensity whilst you progress.

Dry skin

Anyone who uses plaster or clay will find relief from the pH imbalance of the alkali in the material if they wash their hands with cream soap, then rinse well with a one to one solution of white distilled vinegar and water each time.

Dry, ticklish cough

Take half a cupful or less of apple cider vinegar seasoned with salt and pepper. Fill the cup to nearly full with warm water, stir in a raw well-beaten egg slowly. Take a mouthful every 15 or 20 minutes. If the coughing is continuous, dip a cloth rinsed in hot apple cider vinegar seasoned with salt and pepper, and apply round the throat and chest, cover with dry clothes to get up a steam.

Earache

Make up a solution of equal parts of white distilled vinegar and almond oil, and place in an ear dropper. Warm the solution to body temperature by putting the bottle in hot water and then testing it on the back of your wrist. It should feel barely warm. Apply to the affected ear using an ear dropper.

A word of caution: when applying the solution, don't be tempted to push cotton-wool buds into the ear in an attempt to dislodge wax, or because the ear itches. If the ear continues to ache after a day or so, consult your doctor.

Earache is also soothed by a placing a pad of cotton wool soaked in warm castor oil on the bones behind and in front of the ear.

Ear discharge

Take 1 teaspoon of cider vinegar in a glass of water mid morning and mid afternoon. The discharge should shortly disappear.

Eczema

Take 1 teaspoon of apple cider vinegar and 1 teaspoon of honey in a glassful of water 3 times a day with meals. An application of well-diluted apple cider vinegar can also be applied to the skin several times daily i.e. one teaspoon to half a cup of water. Under no circumstances should salt be taken, as this aggravates the eczema condition considerably. There is usually a potassium deficiency in those people suffering from eczema.

Eyes (sore and tired)

Take 2 teaspoons of apple cider vinegar and 2 teaspoons of honey in a glassful of water, 3 times a day. This mixture retards the onset of tired and sore eyes, which are usually apparent in later life, as it supplies them with those vital elements essential to their health and functioning.

Add a dash of salt to freshly cooled boiled water and bathe sore eyes with a clean cloth wetted in the solution. Keep your eyes closed whilst bathing.

Energy drink

Take 2 cupfuls of grape juice, 2 cupfuls of white grape juice, 2 cupfuls of apple juice and 1 cupful of apple cider vinegar. Mix well and refrigerate. Every morning before you do anything else, drink a small cup of it. Each batch lasts a week or two depending on how much you drink each morning. It tastes sort of like a strong wine.

Fatigue

Chronic fatigue is a warning that the body needs some attention. Most people suffering from chronic fatigue do not have enough good, sound sleep. Either they go to bed too late, or they are one of those people who just need more sleep than most. Mix 3 teaspoons of apple cider vinegar to a cup of honey. Take 2 teaspoons of the mixture before retiring. This should induce sound sleep within an hour; if however, you have been unable to sleep within this period repeat the dosage.

Boost your energy during the day by drinking half a tumbler of warm water to which is added 1 teaspoon of apple cider vinegar and 1 teaspoon of honey. Sip slowly.

Fat reducer

Taking a teaspoon of apple cider vinegar with or just before meals to isolate the fat in food as it passes through your system.

To reduce a bulging waistline, make up a mixture of ½ teaspoon of cayenne pepper with 1 teaspoon of baby oil. Apply the mixture to the area and cover with a plastic wrap at bedtime. Warning: Don't use this method if you have a sensitive skin.

Fever calming

Immerse a pair of socks in a mixture of equal parts apple cider vinegar and cold water. Wring them out and place them on the feet of the feverish person. Before the socks have dried completely, re-soak them in the solution and replace. Repeat this process a few times. This method works particularly well with children.

Flatulence

Stop flatulence and passing wind by adding 2 teaspoons of apple cider vinegar to the water when soaking beans or split peas. Add a further 2 teaspoons in the cooking water.

Folliculitis

Inflammation may occur almost anywhere on the skin. It is commonly found on the neck, thighs, buttocks, or armpits, causing a boil, or it may affect the bearded area of the face, leading to pustules. A good way of calming it down is to make a compress: mix 1 part white distilled vinegar to 4 parts lukewarm water in a bowl.

Rinse a clean flannel in the solution and apply it as a compress to the inflamed area for about 20 minutes. It should clear up after a couple of applications.

Food poisoning – prevention

Chopping boards and pastry boards should be scrubbed clean as soon as they have been used to prevent food poisoning germs from harbouring in the cracks. The way to get them clean is to scrub them with salt water, and wash down with white vinegar and put the board in the sunlight to whiten.

Footcare

If you suffer from dry rough feet, simply soak them in warm water, half a cup of white distilled vinegar, and Epsom mineral salts for approximately 30 minutes. Remove and rinse with lukewarm water and a mild soap. Apply pure vitamin E moisturiser or break apart a vitamin E capsule and rub all over the feet and ankle area. Put on a pair of socks and closed shoes. Repeat for about a month and your feet will look and feel more supple.

To warm-up the feet and relieve the cold feelings one has when outdoors in cold winter weather, sprinkle a little cayenne pepper inside the shoes. Due to the warming activity of cayenne pepper, blood is attracted to the region, thus eliminating the condition.

For chronic foot odour, line your shoes with charcoal insoles. For cleanliness, wash your feet 3 to 4 times a week in a footbath containing ½ a cup of apple cider vinegar and warm water.

Hair care

❑ If you have dandruff, apply lavender vinegar liberally to the head, and massage well into the scalp. Afterwards, wash your hair in a good proprietary shampoo designated for your type of hair. Repeat this several times each week until the condition clears up.

❑ To prevent dandruff, pour apple cider vinegar directly into the hair, massaged into the scalp, and leave to dry for a few minutes. Then wash the hair in the normal way. Repeat the process each time you wash your hair.

❑ To keep your hair looking luxuriously shiny, rinse in a solution of ½ cupful of apple cider vinegar mixed with 1 litre of warm water.

❑ To remove sticky sweets from a child's hair, apply white distilled vinegar to dissolve the mess, then comb out and shampoo.

❑ Hair loss is primarily due to a tissue salt deficiency, thus cider vinegar with its 'wonder products' will re-establish a natural balance, and supply the deficiencies where needed. Take 1 teaspoonful in a glass of water in the morning on a regular basis to restore the balance.

❑ Stimulate new growth by vigorously massaging your head with a mixture of cayenne pepper and baby oil every day. Use ¼ teaspoon of pepper to ½ teaspoon of oil. Wash your hair in the normal way after the massage.

❑ To get rid of headlice, treat the hair to a medicated shampoo to get rid of headlice, then get rid of the stubborn hangers-on and live eggs. Rinse the hair thoroughly with equal parts of white distilled vinegar and hot water and comb through with a nit comb. The vinegar helps to dissolve dead nits and wash off their remains. Treating the hair will not be of any use unless you also rid the headlice from the person's bedding and clothing.

❑ Baking soda is great for getting rid of the build-ups of chemicals and muck that some shampoos and hair sprays leave behind. To eliminate all those problems, add a teaspoon of baking soda to your shampoo while you are washing your hair, and then proceed to lather and rinse as normal. If you do this often, be sure to condition your hair as continued use of baking soda could cause it to dry out.

❑ If your hair reacts badly to chlorine in swimming pools – it can turn some dyed blonde hair greenish – then a way around this is during your after-dip shower, once you've dampened your hair with clean water, mix half a cup of lemon juice with a tablespoon of baking soda and while it is still fizzing away, pour it into your hair and work it through. This will make sure that the chlorine is negated.

Hay fever

A tablespoon of honey should be taken after each meal for approximately a fortnight before the onset of the hay fever season. The ordinary dosage of 2 teaspoons of apple cider vinegar and 2 of honey in a glass of water 3 times a day should be maintained during the entire hay-fever season.

Headaches

Many people have had relief from headaches by the use of apple cider vinegar. Equal parts of apple cider vinegar and hot water should be placed in a small basin. When the fumes begin to rise from the basin lean your head over it until the fumes are comfortably strong. Inhale for approximately 50 to 80 breaths. Generally this alleviates the headache considerably, if not entirely.

Heart treatment

Keep your cardiovascular system healthy by sprinkling cayenne pepper on your food daily.

Hand wash

To keep your skin clean and healthy after a busy day in the garden, wash away the dirt on your hands with white distilled vinegar. Follow the washing with a thorough rinsing in cold water and an application of a good skin lotion.

Hangnails

First, wash the hands in white distilled vinegar to cleanse them, then wash with soap and rinse in clean water. Use a good set of nail clippers to carefully snip the hangnails close to the skin surface. Next, gently massage your fingers with a good skin moisturiser. Regular treatments will prevent further problems.

Heart palpitations

A single skipped heartbeat occasionally throughout the day can make you wonder what is going on inside. But as long as you've had the OK from your doctor there should be no cause for concern. Cut down on drugs that contain caffeine, such as diet pills, drink less coffee and tea, and eat less chocolate. Instead, drink more water, and take a garlic capsule everyday, and a teaspoon of apple cider vinegar regularly in a glass of warm water.

Haemorrhoids

The pain of haemorrhoids can be drastically reduced when you add liberal amounts of cayenne pepper to your food.

Hiccups

A popular folklore remedy is to drink 1 tablespoon of undiluted herb vinegar. It is the acidic content of the vinegar that is believed to do the trick, but any other liquid will probably do the same.

A teaspoon of apple cider vinegar relieves hiccups more effectively than anything else, including lemon juice or sugar.

High blood pressure

Take 2 teaspoons of apple cider vinegar and 2 teaspoons of honey in a glass of water – up to three to four times a day, in conjunction with a good diet. It is said that drinking up to 3 cups of cayenne tea a day will improve your blood pressure.

Hunger reducer

A teaspoon of apple cider vinegar in a glass of water, with a bit of honey added for flavour, will take the edge off your appetite and give you an overall healthy feeling.

Insomnia

Take 2 teaspoons of cider vinegar and two of honey in a glass of water before retiring. It would also be beneficial to have a glass of this mixture by the bedside to sip if needed.

Indigestion

Scientists now say that a major cause of dyspepsia (upset stomach) is the bacterial strain, Helicobacter pylori.

- One of the most celebrated antacid remedies is the use of baking soda's medicinal use as a counter-agent against acid indigestion. The formulation is quick and simple to prepare; add ½ a teaspoon of baking soda to half a glass of water and drink immediately.
- If you prefer a fizzy remedy, which can help soothe certain discomforts, add ½ a teaspoon of sugar to the water along with a tablespoon of apple cider vinegar. Again, drink it quickly, while it is still fizzing away.

It is important not to take too much baking soda in this way, however; the maximum dosage is one of these ½ teaspoon formulations every two hours, with no more than 8 in any one 24 hour period. You should not continue this level of dosage daily for more than 2 weeks.

You should not take baking soda or any other antacid when your stomach is too full, so as to avoid possible injury, and you should remember that there are significant differences between heartburn and the more serious stomach complaints such as cramps, aches and so on.

❑ If you don't fancy using baking soda, make up syrup using 1 dessertspoonful of apple cider vinegar and 1 tablespoon of clear honey. Swallow a teaspoon of the syrup, and then slowly sip a cup of boiled, slightly cooled, hot water. Take as often as necessary.

❑ A teaspoon of cayenne pepper sprinkled daily on food stops indigestion and improves the condition of the digestive system.

❑ Heartburn usually occurs after eating, sometimes up to 2 hours later. Taking 1 tablespoon of apple cider vinegar and water before meals can alleviate this very unpleasant feeling. Also, sipping a cupful of warm water laced with apple cider vinegar will help.

Kidneys and bladder

The kidneys and bladder can benefit tremendously by a drinking a cup of comfrey tea first thing in the morning with a teaspoon of apple cider vinegar.

❑ Applying a cayenne pepper poultice over the kidney regions or over the lower back helps in restoring general loss of physical energy or general debility *(See Poultice)*. This external therapy may be combined with the intake of tea made from mistletoe, stinging nettle or a mixture of vervain, mistletoe and eucalyptus.

Look younger

Just 1 cup of cayenne tea sipped slowly each day will boost your immune system and protect you against disease, which can add years to your life. To make yourself look years younger, drink a cup of cayenne tea daily. It will improve the tone of your skin and give you a healthy youthful glow.

Lupus

Lupus often begins with aching muscles and joints, and will persist throughout the sufferer's life. To ease the aches and pains in the hands and feet, try soaking the extremities in a bowl of hot water to which a few tablespoons of apple cider vinegar is added.

Some people get relief by rinsing 2 towels in the solution. First of all, wrap the joint with a hot towel, and then, when it has cooled, wrap with the second towel that has been cooled with ice. Repeat this procedure until relief is obtained. A bag of frozen peas or corn is a good alternative to ice.

Memory

Dramatically sharpen your memory by drinking 3 cups of cayenne tea each day.

Menstruation

Apple cider vinegar regulates and normalises profuse bleeding. The dosage should be 2 teaspoons of apple cider vinegar in a glassful of water three times a day. Diet should also be taken into consideration, as a high animal protein diet together with wheat products will cause considerable pain when the periods begin. In other words, eat such foods in moderation.

Muscle pain

A mixture of ½ teaspoon of cayenne pepper and 1 teaspoon of baby oil will help to reduce muscular aches and pains after exercise.

Nocturnal cramps

Mix 2 tablespoons of apple cider vinegar with 1 cup of honey and store this mixture in an airtight container. Anytime you have trouble getting to sleep, take two teaspoons of the mixture and you'll get a good night's sleep.

Nail hygiene

Painful swellings around your nail folds are typical signs of fungal infection. Unfortunately, infections can spread from your toenails to your fingernails. For a quick remedy start putting a few drops of white distilled vinegar on your nails several times a day, it really works. After washing and scrubbing with soap and water to smooth away dead skin, rinse your hands and feet in white distilled vinegar. Use a good set of nail clippers to carefully pare the nails. Next, gently massage your fingers and toes with a good skin moisturiser. Regular treatments will prevent further problems.

Brittle, cracking, fragile and thin nails are a sign of some deficiency and faulty metabolism in the body. Apple cider vinegar has been known to remedy this particular complaint, with the results of healthy, strong nails. Also any white spots that were present on the nails previously will be eliminated. Dosage being: 2 teaspoons of apple cider vinegar in a glassful of water 3 times a day.

Nausea

When your stomach stops heaving, seek relief with a non-alcoholic drink of ginger cordial. Usually the symptom will go away more quickly if you add a teaspoon of clove vinegar.

Season a cupful of apple cider vinegar with salt and pepper, and take a mouthful just before going to bed.

Neuralgia

The external application of cayenne oil or cayenne liniment helps immensely in relieving the pain associated with neuralgia. In addition to this external treatment, a cup of tea made from herbs like: passion flower, St. John's wort, sage, vervain, basil, lemon balm, etc. helps in relieving pains.

Nicotine craving

If you are trying to give up smoking, new evidence suggests that baking soda may be able to help. Researchers at the world-famous Mayo clinic have found that when you get a craving for a cigarette brought on by nicotine withdrawal, you can get some immediate relief by drinking a bubbling solution of 2 teaspoons of baking soda in a glass of water. This fix cannot be used more than twice a day however, so as to keep your acid balances correct.

Nose bleeds

When a person has a nosebleed without any apparent reason, then 2 teaspoons of apple cider vinegar in a glass of water, 3 times a day will aid in restoring the natural clotting properties of the blood.

Nose (blocked)

To clear a blocked nose, add ¼ of a teaspoon of baking soda to a tablespoonful of water and allow it to dissolve. A drop or two of this mixture in each nostril will soon unblock your nose.

Oral hygiene

- When it comes to brushing your teeth, you can add a little zing to your morning start by dipping the bristles of your toothbrush lightly into baking soda before adding your toothpaste, or even instead of your toothpaste. If you want to make up a home formulation, you can go for simplicity and add some artificial sweetener to plain baking soda for a pleasant tooth powder. Alternatively you can use a fluoride mouthwash to mix up a baking soda paste, and store it in a small jar or tube for use when you need it.
- If you are feeling a bit more adventurous, you may like to make up your own special formulation by mixing 3 tablespoons of baking soda, 1 tablespoon of fine-ground salt,

one tablespoon of glycerine for body, a few drops of boiled cooled water, and perhaps 10 or so drops of a food flavouring concentrate of your choice, such as peppermint or vanilla.

❑ Dry salt sprinkled on your toothbrush makes a good tooth polisher. For cleaner brighter dentures – leave your dentures in white distilled vinegar for about 15 minutes to half an hour, and then brush them thoroughly.

❑ An octogenarian who still has quite a few good teeth that are brilliantly white recommended this tip. Add two tablespoons of white distilled vinegar to a cupful of filtered, boiled water. Use the water for cleaning the teeth both at night and morning.

❑ If you have gum disease (gingivitis), then try making up a paste of 2 thirds baking soda and 1 third hydrogen peroxide. Don't make too much up at any one time though, because hydrogen peroxide breaks down fairly quickly. It is said to be a marvellous aid in the fight against gingivitis.

❑ Sore gums can be soothed by gently rubbing a baking soda paste into them. You can use water to make the paste, or if you prefer, you can use a fluoride mouthwash for extra protection. Talking about extra protection, why not dip your dental floss in baking soda before you use it? It'll help to remove plaque build-up and other bits of dirt and food material.

❑ If you have a tooth brace, you can keep it clean by brushing it with baking soda so that it really gleams.

❑ To keep your toothbrush sparkling clean soak the bristles in white distilled vinegar at least twice a week.

❑ Mildly salted water makes an effective mouthwash. Use it hot for a sore throat gargle. Alternatively, gargle with a pinch of salt and a teaspoon of apple cider vinegar in a cup of tepid water.

- Sore throats can respond well to a baking soda gargle. One tried and tested remedy is to mix equal amounts of baking soda, salt and brown sugar, and to dissolve 2 teaspoons of this mix in a glass of warm water. Gargle with the solution to ease the discomfort, and spit out the mixture afterwards.

- If you prefer to be able to swallow your gargle, dissolve an aspirin in a tablespoonful of boiling water, and add a flat teaspoon of baking soda and a further ½ cup of warm water. Use this as a gargle, and swallow it afterwards.

- Sore throat could result from an infection and irritation in the throat. Often times, it is an indication of a physical ailment. Also, sore throat may result from shouting, smoking, or a sign of general debility.

- Gargling with a mixture of hot cayenne pepper and sea salt dissolved in diluted apple cider vinegar is one of the most useful home-remedies used in combating sore throats and laryngitis by combining analgesic, antimicrobial, and astringent properties in one.

- Alternative, the cayenne pepper, together with the sea salt could be dissolved in diluted lemon juice and use as gargle.

- Herbs, such as sage, thyme, marshmallow, acrimony, and yarrow could be made into an infusion and be used as gargles. 1 to 2 teaspoons of one of the herbs or their combinations could be infused in a teacup of boiling water for 5 to 10 minutes. After filtering, a teaspoon of cayenne pepper is added and used as gargle for sore throats.

- Cayenne pepper mixed with goldenseal and myrrh powder dissolved in water makes an effective gargle for sore throats and laryngitis. These mixtures could also be used as an effective antiseptic mouth wash.

Pick-me-up

Combine raw eggs, vinegar of your choice, and a pinch of black pepper. Blend well before drinking.

Poultice

Cayenne pepper could be applied directly on the skin in the form of herbal poultice. The cayenne pepper is made into a paste by adding hot water. Alternatively, the pepper could be mixed with equal quantity of powdered charcoal and then mixed into a paste with hot water.

The pepper or its mixture with charcoal is spread directly on the affected part, or spread between gauze and placed on the affected part. It is then covered with light cloth or gauze and bandaged loosely.

Shaving foam

You can use a thin paste of baking soda in place of shaving foam; not only will it provide a clean and healthy lubricant for the razor, but baking soda can also work to give relief from shaving rash and razor burns.

Shingles

The pain of shingles may continue long after the pustules and cracks have healed. You can try using an ice pack to numb the nerve endings, but for a homemade treatment that really does work, dab undiluted apple cider vinegar onto the affected area. Do this several times a day, and again at night if you are kept awake by the discomfort. If all else fails, your doctor can prescribe Eumovate cream, which contains clobetasone butyrate, to take away the pain and itching.

Skin problems

- On hot days, combat prickly heat and heat rashes by having a cooling, luke warm shower. Don't use any soap-based cleaner. Once you are dry, rub a little baking soda and water paste into any areas of rash and leave it on. Perhaps the most popular skin-based use for baking soda, however, is as a marvellous anti-spot solution. Add just enough hydrogen peroxide to baking soda to make up a thick paste, and dab it on the offending area before going to bed. Leave it on overnight for maximum anti-zit action.

- If your feet ache and need some reconstitution after a hard day, a foot bath made with ¼ litre of hot water and 4 tablespoons of baking soda will bring blessed relief. It's also great for relieving lingering foot odour. Once you've soaked your feet in this way for a while, you'll also have softened up the skin nicely to make it particularly suitable for beautification; a pumice stone can be used to remove ingrained dirt and dead and callused skin.

- Add a tablespoon of baking soda to the bath water to relieve general skin irritations such as measles and chicken pox.

- To relieve itching on the scalp or body, apply apple cider vinegar. Soak a linen clothe in equal amounts of apple cider vinegar and water; wring out the cloth and apply to the affected part. Rinse off after application..

- To ease windburns, moisten some baking soda and apply directly with a clean damp cloth. Similarly, to ease chapped skin, mix together equal amounts of rosemary vinegar and apple cider vinegar with a few drops of eau de Cologne or perfume. Dab the lotion on the skin, working out very gently from the wrinkles in the skin.

- If you can't use commercial deodorants try spraying with white distilled vinegar under your arms and other areas of the body, you will find that it acts as a natural deodorant. It won't prevent perspiration but it will neutralise body odour. You can also use baking soda in a puffer and apply as an underarm deodorant.

❑ A daily 10 minute bath in hot water (as hot as you can stand) into which is added 7 cups of apple cider can cleanse the body of acid residues. Vinegar baths are also useful as an additional therapy for fungal skin diseases and for treating vaginitis.

❑ Honey water can be used to smooth rough hands if a little is smoothed into the skin every night before bed. To make for yourself, pour 25 grams of runny honey into a 200 millilitre glass jar and add the strained juice of a lemon and zest of 1 orange. Stir together to blend and add 50 millilitres white wine vinegar. Place a lid on the jar and shake thoroughly. Allow the mixture to steep for 3 days, shaking frequently, and then filter and bottle again.

❑ White distilled vinegar promotes skin health; rub on tired, sore or swollen muscles.

❑ Remove liver spots (age spots) by making up a solution by extracting the juice of 1 large onion and mixing with 2 parts of white distilled vinegar. Rub onto the affected skin several times a day. Within a few weeks, this treatment will begin to have its effect.

❑ To remove fruit stains from your hands, rub them with a little white vinegar and wipe with a cloth.

❑ There are several baby and childhood complaints that baking soda can help. To combat cradle cap, make a paste of baking soda and water and gently rub it into baby's head for a moment or two before you wash the hair with a mild shampoo as normal. Alternatively, you can oil the hair with baby oil and then rub the baking soda into the oil. Comb this through gently, loosening any matter, before shampooing out.

- Dry scalp skin can also be fought by mixing 1 part baking soda with 4 parts petroleum jelly and rubbing it into the scalp. Leave this for 15 minutes before washing it out.
- Nappy rash is also well-suited to treatment with baking soda. You can also dissolve 2 teaspoons of baking soda in a pint of warm water to make a pleasant neutralising solution to wipe down baby's bottom. The alkaline action neutralises the acids and odours of urine. You can also add half a cup of baking soda to the water at bath time to help neutralise nappy rash.

Sprains

Soak a bandage in equal amounts of hot soda water, apple cider vinegar, and a pinch of salt. Rinse out and bandage the sprained limb or rub apple cider vinegar on the sprained area with a warm cloth.

Sinusitis

To open up clogged sinuses, use the same remedy given for catarrh. Zinc is supposed to have a good effect on clearing the nose, and a daily zinc supplement may help. Beware of decongestant sprays. Overuse can cause damage to the lining of the nose. An old folk remedy says you should take 1 teaspoon of apple cider vinegar and 1 teaspoon of honey mixed with half a cupful of hot water 4 times a day until relief is felt.

Sunburn

Don't use bubble baths, scented soaps or perfumes when suffering from sunburn; these commodities will only make matters worse. To get relief, you need to cool the skin. Taking a cold bath is very unwise, as it can be too much of a shock to your body. Therefore, to relieve the pain, pat cold white distilled vinegar onto the affected area with a clean cotton-wool swab every 20 minutes.

Alternatively use a ¼ cupful of baking soda mixed into a 2 litre bowl of cool water. Dab the affected area with a clean cotton-wool swab every 20 minutes.

Talc

Because baking soda doesn't contain any other chemicals, it is great for people who suffer from allergic reactions or similar problems. It is safe to use on the inner thighs and pubic regions, too. If you want a slightly smoother action from your talc, then you can mix the baking soda with talcum powder for a really silky effect.

Tinnitus

A common cause of tinnitus and the most simple to remedy is an accumulation of earwax. Once the wax is removed, the sounds will disappear. If it is earwax causing obstruction, soften it with oil. You can make a preparation by adding a few drops of olive oil or almond oil to a cup of water and heating it to body heat. Add a few drops of white distilled vinegar and then, using a dropper, apply 2 or 3 drops in the affected ear.

Tonic 1

Dissolve 2 teaspoons of apple cider vinegar and 2 teaspoons of honey in a glass of warm water. Drink a glass of this tonic every morning and evening for at least 6 weeks. Over time, you will feel revitalised and more energetic.

Tonic 2

For a refreshing bath to soak up aches and pains, add 1 cupful of lavender vinegar and 1 cupful of Epsom salts to the bath water. It works best if used in the morning to get you started, or to revive you before an evening out. Keep the water fairly cool and use a bath mitt to rub down and invigorate the skin. This treatment should not be used for those with high blood pressure or a heart condition.

Toothache

- For instant relief, apply oil of cloves on a cotton-wool bud to the aching tooth. If oil of cloves isn't to hand, take an aspirin. Then there are plenty of oral gels that can be applied; these are especially good if the gums are giving trouble.
- If your tooth is spontaneously throbbing with a dull kind of ache, do contact your dentist urgently, and take painkillers as prescribed. Use, if tolerable, hot and cold mouth washes with a teaspoon of white distilled vinegar added.
- Try the salt and vinegar remedy, which, apparently, works wonders when toothache is caused by gum disorders. Mix 1 teaspoon of salt and 1 teaspoon of apple cider vinegar in half a glassful of warm water and then swish it around your gums. Sometimes this is all you need do to reduce the pain.
- In an emergency rub full strength white distilled vinegar onto a tooth that is aching as well as the surrounding gum. This relief is only temporary, but it works.

Upset stomach

Drink 2 teaspoons apple cider vinegar in 1 cup water to soothe an upset stomach.

Vaginal itching

Vaginal and anal itching can often be relieved in a similar manner. Make a solution of 2 tablespoons of baking soda in 125 millilitres of water. Use as a douche twice a day to rinse out the affected cavity.

Varicose veins

To shrink varicose veins, apply undiluted vinegar to the affected limb. Massage the skin with the bare hands wetted with vinegar. Rub well in.

A compress made with apple cider vinegar helps ease the pain and swelling that can be caused by varicose veins. Soak a towel in apple cider vinegar and then wrap it around the affected areas. Cover with a dry towel; elevate your legs and rest for 30 minutes. If you have sensitive skin, dilute the vinegar with warm water. You can also massage the area with apple cider vinegar to improve blood flow and tighten the tissue. The massage can be done daily.

Weight reducing

Apple cider vinegar will support your efforts to lose weight provided that you are already on a weight-loss diet. The best way to take apple cider vinegar when combining it with a diet is to add 2 teaspoons of apple cider vinegar to a glass of water and drink it either with meals or 30 minutes prior to a meal.

Apple cider vinegar will help your digestive juices to process as well as to assimilate nutrients by helping to break down proteins in the gut, thus helping your body to attain the ideal weight for you.

With most diets you won't see any difference for the first week or so; after that, you should notice a difference and begin losing weight. You will find that taking apple cider vinegar with your diet will not only help to promote weight loss but will also make you feel better, which will make exercise and developing good nutritional habits much easier to do.

Wart remover

Mix 1 part apple cider vinegar to one part glycerine into a lotion and apply daily to warts until they dissolve.

Part Three

Cookery

WHAT BOOK about kitchen cupboard healers could possibly be complete without taking a look at the range of culinary uses to which they can be put? Here, we've gathered some of the best tips from around the world. There is something for every palate in here, and every one makes excellent use of the quartet. Just take a browse through and when you find a tip you like the look of, give it a try!

Apple cinnamon vinegar

Apple cinnamon vinegar is ideal for improving the taste of homemade pâtés.

Baking powder

To make your own baking powder, stir and sift together 2 parts of cream of tartar to 1 part baking soda and 1 part cornflour.

Barbecue sauce

You can heat up a barbecue sauce or meat marinade with a shake of cayenne pepper.

Boiled ham

Add a little cider or wine vinegar to the water in which you boil ham. It will draw out the salty taste and improve the flavour.

Boiled meat

When boiling tough meats, add a teaspoon of white distilled vinegar to the water to make it more tender.

Bread

For a shiny crust on homemade bread and rolls, brush the crusts with white distilled vinegar just before they have finished baking, then return to the oven to finish baking.

Cabbage

Avoid cabbage smells when cooking by adding white distilled vinegar to the water.

Cheese freshness

To keep cheese fresh and moist, wrap it in a cloth dampened in white vinegar and put it into an airtight wrapping or container.

Chocolate cake

Make a better chocolate cake by adding a teaspoon white distilled vinegar to your cake mix.

Cooking odours

Boil a teaspoon of white vinegar mixed in a cup of water to eliminate unpleasant cooking odours.

Dips and sauces

Try adding cayenne pepper to salsa, avocado dip, taco, and sauces for extra zesty flavour.

Egg substitute

If you are short of an egg in a cake recipe, you can replace the egg with 1 tablespoon of white distilled vinegar without affecting the result. This works best if you are using a raising agent or self-raising flour.

Firmer gelatines

Add a teaspoon of white vinegar to any gelatine recipe in hot summer months to keep moulded salads and desserts firm.

Flavouring

You can really liven up a tin of soup or mediocre gravy with just a teaspoon of wine vinegar. It adds flavour and tastes fresher.

Fluffier meringue

For a really fluffy meringue, add ¼ teaspoon of white vinegar to 3 egg whites.

Fruit – cooking

Add a teaspoon of white distilled vinegar when cooking fruit to improve the flavour.

Fruit gelatine

Add a tablespoon of white distilled vinegar to fruit gelatine to hold it firm.

Ham

Rub white distilled vinegar on the cut end of uncooked ham to prevent mould.

Herbs

Steep your favourite herbs in herb vinegar until you have a pleasing taste and aroma.

Icing

To improve sugar icing add a drop of white distilled vinegar when mixing.

Lemon replacement

Use your favourite flavoured vinegar instead of lemon on fried and broiled foods.

Marinades

To use up all those bits of tomato sauce or chutney etc. that come in bottles add some vinegar of your choice and some olive oil. Shake the bottle before using. The liquid will pour out easily; this makes the base for marinades, just add onion, garlic and spices.

Meringues

For a fluffy meringue beat 3 egg whites with a teaspoon of white distilled vinegar.

Olives

Olives will keep indefinitely if covered with the vinegar of your choice and refrigerated.

Omelettes

You can add a great taste to omelettes with tomatoes, onions, peppers, and a pinch of cayenne pepper added to the eggs.

Onion odours

A little white vinegar rubbed on your fingers before and after slicing onions will quickly remove the onion odour.

Pasta

To make pasta less sticky put a few drops of white distilled vinegar in the water as it boils.

Peppers

When bottling peppers place them in a sterilised jar and finish filling with boiling vinegar of your choice.

Pickling remedies

Pickling is the preserving of food in an acid (usually vinegar), and it is this acid environment that prevents undesirable bacteria growth. However, how and what kind of acid gets into the liquid is what can cause some confusion about the use of salt.

Most pickled foods are salted or soaked in brine first to draw out moisture that would dilute the acid that is added to pickle the food.

The food can be placed in brine (salt and water) – this is what causes confusion. Even though it may seem that pickling can be done with either an acid (vinegar, etc) or salt, is not strictly true. That is because the amount of salt in the solution is carefully measured to allow natural fermentation, which produces lactic acid. So pickled foods that are made with brine (salt and water) are really made with an acid, but instead of directly adding acid, conditions are created so that the fermentation creates its own acid. This is a tricky process because just enough salt needs to be added to prevent the growth of undesirable bacteria, and the correct temperature maintained, to allow the growth of several specific bacteria that produce lactic acid.

Some cucumber pickles are made with a combination of both methods. They are soaked in strong brine with vinegar added in specific proportions so that they still ferment and produce additional acid (lactic acid).

Soft or slippery pickles

- ❏ The brine may be too weak. Maintain 10-12% salt concentration. Alternatively the vinegar may be too weak. Use vinegar of 4-6% acidity.
- ❏ Could be caused by the pickles being stored at a temperature too high during curing/brining. Optimum temperature should be about 70°-75° F for growth of the organisms necessary for fermentation.
- ❏ Insufficient amount of brine. Keep pickles immersed in the brine.

Strong, bitter taste

- ❏ Spices cooked too long in vinegar, or too many spices used. Follow directions for amount of spices to use and the boiling time.
- ❏ Vinegar may be too strong. Strong vinegars should be diluted to 4-6% acidity.

Hollow pickles

- Large pickles will bloat at 10-12% brine solution. Use smaller pickles to brine.
- A common cause is improper curing. Curing is complete when the bubbling ceases, usually after about 6 weeks.
- Long lapse of time between harvesting and processing. Pickling process should be started within 24 hours after gathering.
- Poor quality pickles. Remove hollow pickles during washing, hollow pickles will be seen to float. Remove and use for relishes.

Shrivelled pickles

- Placing pickles in too strong a brine, heavy syrup, or too strong a vinegar. Strength should be between 10-12% brine, use the correct amount of sugar called for in the recipe, and the vinegar should be 4-6% acidity.
- Long lapse of time between harvesting and pickling. Pickles should be placed in the brine within 24 hours after gathering.

Dark or discoloured pickles

- Minerals in hard water can cause discolouration. Use soft water.
- Ground spices can also cause discolouration. Use whole spices.
- Spices left in the jar when pickling will cause discolouration. They should be placed loosely in a cheesecloth bag so that they can be removed before bottling.
- The use of brass, iron, copper, or zinc utensils during preparation will cause discolouration. Always use, glass, stainless steel, or stoneware utensils.

Spotted, dull, or faded colour

- Pickles have not been cured (brined) correctly. The

concentration of brine must be 10-12% salt.

❑ Incorrect storage in excessive light will cause the pickles to fade. They should be stored in a dark, dry, cool place.

❑ Poor quality pickles can cause spotting and fading when pickled. Always buy good quality produce.

Scum on cucumber brine while curing

This is caused by wild yeast, moulds, and bacteria that feed on the acid thus reducing the constituent in the brine. Remove scum as often as needed.

Pie crust

Add 1 tablespoon of white distilled vinegar to your pastry recipe for an exceptional crust.

Poaching eggs

Add a teaspoon of white vinegar to the water in which you are poaching eggs. When the water is hot, swirl the water around with a spoon and then drop the egg gently into the water. This way, the whites will stay better formed around the yolk.

Potatoes

Prevent discolouration of peeled potatoes by adding a few drops of white distilled vinegar to the water when cooking. They will keep fresh for days in fridge.

Preserves

When storing home cooked preserves, make them last longer by wiping the outside of the jars with white distilled vinegar to prevent mould-producing bacteria.

Rice

Add 1 teaspoon of white distilled vinegar to cooking water for fluffier rice.

Sauces

Over sweet commercial sauces and other condiments will last long by adding white distilled vinegar.

Sour cream

To make your own sour cream, blend together 1 cupful cottage cheese, ¼ cupful skimmed milk and 1 teaspoon white distilled vinegar.

Souring the milk

If you have a recipe that calls for sour milk, add a bit of white distilled vinegar to the milk to sour it.

Storing cheese

Keep your cheeses fresher and longer by wrapping it in a vinegar-soaked cloth and keeping it in a sealed container.

Storing vinegar

'How long will vinegar keep on the shelf?' Before foodstuffs were marketed with 'Sell By' and 'Use By' dates, indicating how long the product will remain edible, no one thought about the keeping qualities of produce, let alone how long vinegar would keep. However the Vinegar Institute decided to investigate, and conducted a study on the subject. They announced that its shelf life is almost indefinite. Because of its acidity and preservative nature, it does not even need refrigeration. Some changes were observed in flavoured types of vinegars, such as colour, haze and sediment. However, these were considered to be only aesthetic changes, leaving the quality of the product unchanged. It was noted that white vinegar remained virtually unchanged over an extended period of time.

Tartar sauce and dressings

Spice up your tartar sauce and dressings with a pinch of cayenne pepper.

Tenderising marinade

Vinegar is a fine tenderiser for tough meats or game. Make a marinade in the proportion of ½ cup of cider vinegar to a cup of liquid bouillon. Marinate the meat in a covered dish in a refrigerator for a minimum of 2 hours.

Tinned fish and shrimps

To give tinned fish and shrimps a freshly caught taste, marinate them in a mixture of 1 tablespoon of sherry and 2 tablespoons of the vinegar of your choice for 30 minutes.

Washing vegetables

Remove dirt and grime by adding a tablespoon of baking soda to the water when washing vegetables and fruit. Just sprinkle it into the water, soak and then rinse well.

Whiter fish

Try soaking fish in vinegar and water before cooking. You'll get a whiter, less 'fishy'-tasting fish. Use 2 tablespoons of white vinegar per litre of water. Let fish fillets soak in it for 20 minutes before cooking.

Whiter cauliflower

Add a spoonful of vinegar to cooking water to make cauliflower white and clean.

Other Books from Windsor

MUSTARD

—

The Ultimate
Kitchen Condiment

MUSTARD

The History of Mustard

The use of mustard seeds has been known from the earliest recorded times and is described in Indian and Sumerian texts dating back to 3000BC. Although not widely documented in the past as a condiment, mustard has been used for other purposes for thousands of years. It was once used as a stimulant and diuretic in the Middle East where it has long been regarded as an aphrodisiac and an important spice that is used in their traditional dishes. The literary evidence of early centuries indicates that it was used in Rome as early as 42AD. In the 9th Century French monasteries were earning considerable income from mustard preparations made up by the monks. By the 13th Century, mustard was being offered by Parisian sauce-hawkers, who walked the streets peddling their savoury wares.

Throughout the Middle Ages the wonderful aromas and tastes produced by mustard, as well as its other benefits, were well known throughout the civilised world, and had become a standard ingredient in early cookbooks. The *Viandier of Taillevent* refers to it several times, and gives at least one recipe for making it. *Le Menagier de Paris* gives a recipe and advises the reader to buy it from the sauce merchant (depending on the version). Both *The Forme of Cury* and *Das Buoch Von Guter Spise* include recipes for a mustard sauce for preserving fruits and vegetables.

In spite of its general use in middle class and upper class households of the 17th and 18th Centuries, the popularity of mustard began to decline, mainly because of the interest in new spices being brought back from the Americas and the Far East at that time. However, by the turn of the 19th Century there was a revival of interest, and the city of Dijon became known as the capitol of mustard production when, in 1856, Burgundian Jean Naigeon substituted verjuice for the vinegar in prepared mustard. The use of verjuice resulted in a mustard that was less acidic than France had tasted before, and the smooth, suave condiment we call Dijon assumed its place in history.

The Preparation of Mustard

There are three British species, black mustard (B. nigra), wild mustard or charlock (B. arvensis), and white mustard (B. alba). Commercially made mustard is a mixture of the seeds of black mustard and white mustard, ground and mixed with wheat flour and coloured with turmeric.

All mustard preparations are made in relatively the same way. The seed must be crushed, and the hull and bran sifted out. It may then go through further grinding and crushing. The mustard is then mixed, in some cases simmered, and then cooled. Some mustard is aged in large containers before it is bottled and shipped to retailers. Mustard powder, when purchased ready for the table, is mixed with either water, wine, vinegar, beer, or a combination of several of these liquids, along with seasonings and other flavourings.

English mustard is the strongest variety, French mustards are milder, German and Austrian ones are both mild and sweet, and American mustards generally have a completely different, creamy, spreading texture with a mild sugary flavour. All mustards can be used for cooking, or served plain, but Dijon is probably the best to cook with.

Nutrition

Mustard is an annual herb of the Cruciferae family. It contains large amounts of beta-carotene and vitamin C that are important antioxidants. Much research is continuing in order to understand fully why mustard appears to have cancer-preventative properties. Mustard greens are also a source of calcium that can be important to lactose intolerant individuals. Mustard greens also contain a significant amount of iron.

Mustard contains about 30 per cent protein, but does not contain antigrowth factors like those found in soybeans or the anti-thyroid compound common to related spices. Its higher protein content is of particular interest when applied to processed meats. The vegetable oil of mustard is nutritionally similar to other oils and makes up 28% to 36% of the seed. The antioxidant properties of mustard help to protect the oil from becoming rancid, thus contributing to a long shelf life.

Flavour

The characteristic flavour of mustard is derived from the oil components of whole seed, which is used for its rubefacient action when applied medicinally. When used as a spice it is commonly regarded for its piquant flavour. English mustard like other 'hot' flavours, lingers on the tongue giving a pleasant tingling after-effect. Others, such as American mustard, present themselves quickly, then dissolve and leave little or no after-taste.

Although taste is largely a personal choice, there are certain decisive factors to consider when appraising individual recipes. The mustard should be wholly pleasing to the palate. It should not be too salty; it should, to some extent, have a sharp tang, but not too excessive. Its flavours should be well balanced, with no single element dominating.

Texture is important, it should be smooth or, in the case of coarse-grain mustard, satisfyingly granular, not gritty or tough. Consistency should be adequately thick so that when spooned, it easily holds its shape, but should not be so thick as to be cloying or tongue-coating.

Mustard

Cultivation and Harvest

As well as using mustard as an addition to recipes or as a condiment, it can be used in the form of 'mustard greens', which are a very tasty salad accompaniment. They are tender and flavoursome, and are quickly and easily grown by even the most inexperienced.

Do not cover the seed with soil when sowing. It is not necessary, and when covered it is most difficult to remove various particles of earth, or to clean it properly of grit, etc. When sown in frames on hot-beds, in the open, or on the ground, all that is required is to obtain a level surface, scatter the seed evenly over it, water well, and cover with a mat until it is well rooted. When exposed to the light, water frequently. It is best to make a succession of sowings and not sow too much at one time, as it soon grows too old, and gets hot and tough.

The seed retains its germinating power for four years. It will grow to four or five inches long, and will be fit for inclusion in salads eight days after being sown, provided that it is kept well watered. The green leaves can also be cooked, the older leaves tasting better after cooking. Avoid yellow, over mature plants that have gone to seed or with yellow flowers attached.

Storage

Store unwashed greens in the same way as spinach. Put in a plastic bag and store in the drawer of the refrigerator. They will keep for about three days; if wrapped in moist kitchen paper they should keep for up to five days. The flavour may intensify in the refrigerator during the longer five day storage.

Home freezing is not the best way to preserve an over abundance of mustard greens and is not recommended. Like other vegetables they need to be quickly deep frozen for them to be at their best when taking from the freezer.

Mustard and Health

There is little doubt that the best way to obtain mustard is to grow your own. In this way it can be guaranteed to be fresh and at its most potent as regards vitamins, minerals and curative properties. Since early times when only herbs were available to the common people, it was well known that mustard could stimulate the appetite and digestion. It was prescribed for clearing blocked sinuses in much the same way as chillies, which are said to be as effective as commercial decongestants.

Mustard increases the circulation of the blood, hence the use of mustard poultices. Cold feet can be warmed if mustard powder is sprinkled in your socks. It is also claimed to save your toes from frostbite; a similar claim is also made about cayenne pepper and other spices containing volatile oils. A pinch of mustard and a teaspoon of honey added to hot water is said to cure a hacking cough, as well as curing hiccups. To clear a stuffy nose, spread mustard generously over a cracker, and take a few bites. This clears it up in seconds!

One of mustard's greatest health benefits is that it provides tremendous flavour for few calories and little fat. A gram of mustard flour contains just 4.3 calories and simple mustard preparations can be eaten with impunity by nearly everyone. Mustard itself contains no cholesterol, only trace amounts of vegetable fat, and is between 25-32% protein, depending on the variety of plant. Leaf mustard contains calcium, phosphorus, magnesium, and Vitamin B. The essential oil in mustard inhibits growth of certain yeasts, moulds, and bacteria, enabling mustard to function as a natural preservative.

Quick Tips

- Make a paste with mustard and spread on the back of a loose tile to secure it to the wall. It acts like plaster!

Mustard

- Used as a fertiliser on daffodils: it will enhance their colour.
- Add a pinch of mustard to chicken feed; it will stimulate egg production.
- To mend a leaky car radiator temporarily: pour the contents of a 50 gram tin of mustard into the radiator while the engine is running.
- Dust plants in the garden with mustard powder to rid them of insect pests.
- Add 2 teaspoons of mustard powder to a litre of water when watering vegetables, it will stop worms attacking the roots.
- Having trouble with ants? Sprinkle mustard over their trail and they won't cross it.
- After handling onions or garlic, rub some mustard on your hands and rinse with warm water to remove the odour.

Mustard in the Kitchen

Mustard is a traditional supplement in the kitchen. Its emulsifying characteristics help bind sauces, and as a condiment, it is used out of the jar or bottle to enhance sandwiches and other prepared foods. A simple piece of grilled fish is enlivened by a spoonful of your favourite mustard, and certain foods such as roast beef, for example, and sausages, are rarely served without a spoonful of mustard on the side.

Add mustard to dishes towards the end of cooking as the flavour of mustard is lost on heating. Many dishes are vastly improved when mustard is added, but it must be done with an expert sense of knowing when to pause. A delicate taste can easily be lost by the overindulgence of a mustard loving chef.

As a Condiment

- When breading chicken or chops, add a tablespoon of mustard to the bread mixture.
- Combine French mustard with mayonnaise as a sauce for avocados.

Mustard

- Before cooking live clams or mussels, put them in a bucket of water with a few teaspoons of dry mustard to make them spit out the grit and sand.
- Make tuna fish sandwiches with a dash of mustard to give extra zing.
- Some salad cream mixed with a tablespoon of mustard makes hotdogs and sandwiches taste really great.
- Always put a teaspoon of mustard in stir-fries to give it that extra taste.
- When mixing mustard powder with water, use cold water, mix slowly, and let stand for ten minutes. This improves the taste and 'kick'.
- Rub a little mustard on fish fillets before cooking them. This makes the fish taste fresher.
- Try mixing mustard with Tabasco or soy sauce for something different and interesting.

MUSTARD RECIPES

Honey Mustard

¼ cup dry mustard
½ cup honey
½ cup brown sugar
¼ cup red wine vinegar
¼ cup olive oil
1 dessertspoon Worcestershire sauce

Combine all ingredients in a small bowl with a wire whisk until smooth. Pour into a small non-metal container and refrigerate overnight. Stir before serving.

Hot and Sweet Mustard

4 egg lightly beaten
½ cup brown sugar
50 grams mustard powder
1 cup apple cider vinegar
1 teaspoon salt
1½ teaspoons cayenne pepper
½ cup butter - melted

Combine all ingredients in the top of a double boiler. Cook over low heat, stirring constantly, until thickened (about 10 minutes). Cool and pour into a container. Store in refrigerator.

Herb Mustard

Tarragon - finely chopped
mustard powder
herb vinegar

Mix well. This should be eaten within a few hours of preparation.

Black Pepper Mustard

½ cup mustard powder
½ cup cold water
¾ cup all-purpose flour
2 tablespoons syrup
1½ teaspoons salt
¾ teaspoon coarsely ground black pepper
½ cup white wine vinegar

Whisk the mustard powder with the cold water in a medium sized bowl. Set aside for 10 minutes. Add the rest of the ingredients and stir until smooth and creamy. Serve immediately or refrigerate in an airtight container for up to 6 months. This mustard makes a good, piquant, sandwich spread.

English Pub Mustard

¾ cup sour cream
½ teaspoon mustard
½ teaspoon black pepper
½ level teaspoon salt
½ teaspoon garlic powder
1 teaspoon Worcestershire sauce
1½ cups mayonnaise
110g bleu cheese - crumbled

Blend all ingredients except the cheese and mayonnaise at low speed in a blender. Add the mayonnaise and blend for a further ½ minute at low speed and then for 2 minutes at medium speed. Crumble cheese into mixture by hand, and then blend at low speed for no more than 4 minutes. Refrigerate 24 hours before use.

Dijon-Style Mustard

¾ cup mustard
¼ cup very cold water
1 cup cider apple vinegar
1 cup dry white wine
½ cup finely chopped onion
¼ cup finely chopped shallots
3 tablespoons crushed garlic
1 bay leaf
2 teaspoons ground black peppercorns
4 whole juniper berries
2 tablespoons cold fresh lemon juice
2 teaspoons sea salt
2 teaspoons brown sugar

Stir together the mustard and water in a bowl to make a paste. Combine the vinegar, wine, onion, shallots, garlic, bay leaf, peppercorns, and juniper berries in a saucepan and bring the mixture to a simmer over moderate heat. Simmer until reduced by two thirds. Strain mixture, cover and chill. Stir the chilled vinegar reduction into the mustard paste. Add the lemon juice, salt and sugar and stir to combine. Let the mixture stand for at least 20 minutes.

Transfer the mustard mixture to a saucepan: bring to a simmer over a low heat and cook for 15 minutes. Remove from heat and allow to cool. Transfer to a sterile jar and seal tightly. Store on a dark, cool shelf for at least a month or 6 weeks before using. Mustard should be refrigerated once open and will keep for 6 months.

SPECIAL REPORT

Ginger stops the pain of arthritis
- fast and safely

An astounding new study has revealed that a regular intake of ordinary ginger can bring tremendous relief to people afflicted by a wide variety of rheumatoid and arthritic diseases. Taken in the right dosage, the scientists concluded that the spice can not only drastically ease the at times extremely severe pain caused by these ailments but also considerably reduce the swelling that usually accompanies them. What's more, it appears that this form of treatment, unlike many of those currently favoured by conventional medicine, is totally free from any harmful side-effects.

GINGER, an ordinary kitchen spice, is being hailed by medical researchers as an extremely effective wonder remedy with incredible powers to stop or drastically reduce the excruciating pain of arthritis and rheumatism. What's more, the tasty and pungent herb brings relief to sufferers without exposing them to the risk of the many unpleasant - and potentially dangerous - side-effects which are often involved in other forms of treatment.

Although scientists had long thought that ginger could be useful in treating arthritic diseases, the full extent of the spice's almost miraculous powers has only come to light recently when two top scientists in Denmark published a research paper that proved beyond doubt that ordinary ginger can be a marvellous remedy for those afflicted by rheumatism and other musculoskeletal disorders. Here are some of the key points revealed by their major study into the effects of ginger consumption in providing relief from pain and swelling in a group of patients afflicted by rheumatoid arthritis ..... and osteoarthritis: ....

- Considerably more than half of the patients who took ginger regularly said that it had brought them "marked" relief from their symptoms.

- Of the remaining patients, around a half of these had found that taking the spice had provided either "moderate" or "minimal" relief.

Just how effective the spice was in controlling both pain and swelling varied somewhat according to whether the spice was being used to control the symptoms of rheumatoid arthritis or osteoarthritis. Here are the study's findings in greater detail:

- Nearly three quarters (in fact, 74%) of the patients with rheumatoid arthritis reported that taking ginger brought them "marked" relief from pain. Lesser relief, but still described as "moderate" was experienced by a further 11%, while 4% said that their relief was only "minimal". Of all the patients in this group, only roughly one in nine (11%) said that taking ginger had made no appreciable difference to their level of pain.

- As far as ginger's effect in reducing the swellings caused by rheumatoid arthritis was concerned, nearly six out of ten patients (59%) said that taking the spice had brought "marked" relief, with a further 18% reporting a "moderate" improvement. Nearly a quarter (23%) of the patients said that the ginger had made no difference to their swellings.

Just as astounding were the results when the effect of ginger upon patients with osteoarthritis

were analysed. The researchers found that in this group:

- More than half (55%) of the patients reported a "marked" improvement in the amount of pain they suffered, with a further 22% saying that the ginger had brought a "moderate" improvement. Somewhat less than a quarter of the patients reported "minimal" or no improvement (11% and 12% respectively).

- Broadly similar results were obtained about ginger's effectiveness in controlling swelling in osteoarthritis: exactly half of the patients said that the spice had brought "marked" improvement; 20% reported a "moderate" improvement; and 10% and 20% respectively said that there had been "minimal" or no improvement.

ASTOUNDING RESULTS

By any standards, these are astounding results and clearly demonstrate that ginger can be every bit as effective - and often more so - than the best of modern drugs in controlling the symptoms of arthritic disease. Of course, the ginger therapy also brings an additional bonus of inestimable value in that its use is not accompanied by any of the distressing and painful side-effects often produced by drugs commonly used to treat arthritis, these often bringing on very severe stomach upsets or even provoking gastrointestinal bleeding. To illustrate just how effective ginger can be, this is what happened to three representative patients whose case histories form part of the Danish study:

- Rheumatoid arthritis was first diagnosed in patient A when he was 50 years old. Shortly thereafter he started adding raw or fresh ginger to his diet every day, mainly using it to season lightly cooked vegetable or meat dishes. Within a month of doing this, there was evident and marked relief in both pain and swelling. After taking the ginger for three months, the patient was totally free of pain and swelling. Nearly 14 years have gone by since then without any relapse of the symptoms.

- Patient B was a 69-year-old woman afflicted by severe osteoparthritis affecting several vertebrae in her back, the knees and elbows, and her right thumb. Following her diagnosis in 1974, she was put on antiarthritis drugs, but these produced several unpleasant side-effects. Four years ago, she started taking a significant amount of powdered ginger daily, since then settling down to two grams daily. Within four months, her symptoms began to ease considerably and two months thereafter she stopped taking antiarthritis drugs. Originally, her osteoarthritis made it impossible for her to turn her head to the left and look upward. She can do this now, although with a little care.

- Patient C was a 49-year-old man who was diagnosed as having "muscular arthritis" five years ago. Although prescribed analgesics to control both the pains in various muscles and joints, his symptoms became steadily worse, their intensity increasing to the point where he had to stay in bed at various times and was unable to work. Recently, he started taking one teaspoonful of powdered ginger daily. Within two weeks, his pains reduced markedly and then disappeared completely shortly thereafter.t

HOW DOES GINGER WORK?

Exactly why taking ginger can produce such dramatic results is not yet fully by understood by scientists, but Dr Tariq Mustafa, of the Institute of Biology at Odense University, who jointly headed the Danish study with Dr K. C. Srivastava, of the Institute of Community Health at the same university, said: "We think that ginger inhibits two of the enzymes that cause arthritis pain." More specifically, he explained that it was likely that ginger brought about improvements by "interfering with the production and release of products of lipid membranes, peptides and proteins, and amino acids," adding that although this was still mostly speculation, the current experimental data and observations of others suggested that ginger could be a dual inhibitor of eicosanoid synthesis, inhibiting both cyclooxygenase and lypoxygenase products.

Ginger, in fact, is an extremely complex substance, and its essential oil contains more than 200 volatiles, the actions of most which remain still poorly understood. Other major studies have also endorsed the spice's remarkable properties - for example~ scientists at Cornell University's prestigious Medical College found that ginger contained an anti-clotting agent that thinned the blood, so greatly reducing the risk of stroke and heart disease. Other research projects have shown that the spice can also be valuable in lowering blood cholesterol, preventing headaches, and relieving headaches and migraines.

HOW MUCH GINGER HOW OFTEN?

The patients in the Danish study self-administered the spice and the typical dose ranged between 1 and 2 grams daily, the equivalent respectively of roughly of one half to one teaspoonful. Pointing out that ginger was listed by the American Food and Drug Administration as being "Generally Recognised as Safe" (GRAS), Dr Mustafa said that "accordingly, one should not have worries if ginger is consumed in amounts normally available through food for any length of time."

Invariably, any improvements noted by patients were maintained as long as they kept taking the ginger. When some patients stopped their daily dose, many of them suffered a return of some of their symptoms within a few weeks. However, after resuming their ginger therapy, these patients found that soon thereafter they once again experienced the same degree of relief from pain and swelling as previously.

Scientists have long sought a better way to treat arthritic diseases than through the drug-based therapies currently used by mainstream medicine and it looks like the research from Denmark may well mark the starting point of a revolutionary new approach that will end the daily agony suffered by the millions of people in the world with arthritis. Just how important the Danish findings are becomes immediately apparent when you consider the following statistics about arthritis and rheumatism: these diseases affect an estimated 20 million people in Britain today; they are also the biggest single cause of severe disability in the country, as well as accounting for the loss of more than 80 million working days every year.

Staggering though these figures are, they can not even begin to reflect the untold personal misery and pain that lie behind them. Doctors, who are only too well aware of the devastating effect that arthritis and rheumatism can have on severely afflicted patients, have hitherto had relatively little choice in prescribing treatments, these usually consisting primarily of painkillers taken orally or administered through injections, or, in certain very severe cases, surgery. Additionally, other treatments used with varying degrees of success include physiotherapy, the application of heat or electrical stimulation to affected joints, and suggestions for lifestyle adjustments that can make the diseases easier to live with. All of these approaches have their potential problems: the prolonged use of drugs can lead to serious side-effects; the relief provided by physiotherapy and similar treatments is all too often temporary; lifestyle changes can be extremely difficult to bring about; and the results obtained by surgery can be very variable.

Because of the limitations and difficulties surrounding current treatment methods, it's therefore hardly surprising that the Danish findings are seen as a major breakthrough that is likely to herald a whole new era in treating arthritic and rheumatic diseases.

Eager though the medical fraternity may be to further explore ginger's wonder powers, it is expected that it may nevertheless still be some time before its use becomes generalised, as further confirmatory research will be needed until doctors fully accept the spice as a better alternative to drug-based painkillers. In the meantime, however, there is little to stop you from trying this out for yourself, providing you follow some simple guidelines, including:

- Never attempt to make your own diagnosis. If you're having frequent or severe problems with your joints, don't just assume that these are probably due to arthritis or rheumatism, but consult your family doctor. The chances are that your self-diagnosis will have been correct, but it's also possible that your problems may have been symptoms resulting from some other underlying disease which may need different and possibly urgent treatment.

- If your doctor has prescribed any medication for you, never discontinue this -even if only temporarily - nor alter the dosage you're taking without obtaining his prior approval.

- Before taking any other form of treatment - even when it's something as straightforward as ginger, which after all is an ordinary kitchen spice that most of us eat in varying quantities throughout our lives - do check this out first with your doctor as there could just be some special reasons why this could be inadvisable in the specific circumstances of your case.

7